Spring Harvest Praise 2004

Equipping the Church for action

Copyright and photocopying

Acknowledgements

Scripture quotations taken from the HOLY BIBLE, NEW INTERNATIONAL VERSION.
Copyright ©1973, 1978, 1984 by International Bible Society. Used by permission of Hodder and Stoughton Limited. All rights reserved. "NIV" is a registered trade mark of International Bible Society. UK trademark number 1448790

Spring Harvest wishes to acknowledge and thank the following people for their help in the compilation and production of this songbook: Trine Crouch, Cheryl Jenkinson, Graham Kendrick, Deborah Lugg, John Pantry, David Peacock, Sue Rinaldi, Kate Silber, Kate Simmonds, Adrian Thompson, and Spring Harvest Head Office staff. Thank you to Marie Birkinshaw, Mark Earey, Mel Holden, Northumbria Community, Paul Sheppy, Joy Townhill, The Archbishops Council and The Society of St Francis for liturgy and prayers.

Layout by Spring Harvest
Cover Design by Adept Design
Printed in the UK by Halcyon

Published by Spring Harvest, 14 Horsted Square, Uckfield, East Sussex, TN22 1QG, UK.
Spring Harvest. A Registered Charity.
Distributed by ICC, Silverdale Road, Eastbourne, East Sussex, BN20 7AB, UK.

ISBN 1-899788-492

Spring Harvest Praise 2004

1
ABOVE ALL POWERS

above all kings,
above all nature and all created things;
above all wisdom
and all the ways of man,
you were here before the world began.

Above all kingdoms,
above all thrones,
above all wonders the world has ever known;
above all wealth
and treasures of the earth,
there's no way to measure what you're worth.

Crucified, laid behind the stone;
you lived to die, rejected and alone;
like a rose, trampled on the ground,
you took the fall, and thought of me,
above all.

Paul Baloche & Lenny Leblanc. Copyright © 1999
Integrity's Hosanna! Music/Sovereign Music UK & Lensongs Publishing

2
ALL AROUND YOUR THRONE

there are angels singing.
All around your world
there are voices singing.

Holy, holy, holy is the Lord.
Holy, holy, holy is the Lord.

All around your throne
there are praises rising.
All around your world
men and women rising, singing:

Holy, holy, holy is the Lord.
Holy, holy, holy is the Lord.

All around your throne
holy ground is burning.
All around your world
there is faith returning.

From a whisper to a loud shout,
the sound of freedom will ring out.
And we say 'Yes Lord, we are ready'
to be a living sacrifice.'

Sue Rinaldi. Copyright © 2004 Thankyou Music
adm. UK & Europe by Kingsway Music. Used by permission.

2a   Collect for Palm Sunday

Almighty and everlasting God
who in your tender love towards the human race
sent your Son our Saviour Jesus Christ
to take upon him our flesh
and to suffer death upon the cross:
grant that we may follow the example of his patience and humility,
and also be made partakers of his resurrection;
through Jesus Christ your Son our Lord,
who is alive and reigns with you,
in the unity of the Holy Spirit,
one God, now and for ever.
Amen

From Common Worship: Services and Prayers for the Church of England
Copyright © The Archbishops' Council 2000

3
ALLELUIA, SING TO JESUS!

his the sceptre, his the throne:
alleluia! his the triumph,
his the victory alone.
Hear the songs of holy Zion
thunder like a mighty flood:
'Jesus out of every nation
has redeemed us by his blood!'

Alleluia! not as orphans
are we left in sorrow now:
Alleluia! he is near us;
faith believes, but knows not how.
Though the cloud from sight received him
whom the angels now adore,
shall our hearts forget his promise,
'I am with you evermore?'

Alleluia, Jesus is King.
Alleluia, let angels sing.
(Repeat)

Alleluia! bread of heaven,
here on earth our food, our stay:
alleluia! here the sinful
come to you from day to day.
Intercessor, friend of sinners,
earth's redeemer, plead for me,
where the songs of all the sinless
sweep across the crystal sea.

continued over...

Alleluia! King eternal,
you, the Lord of lords we own;
alleluia! born of Mary,
earth your footstool, heaven your throne;
you, within the veil have entered,
robed in flesh, our great high priest;
yours the blood and yours the body,
in our eucharistic feast.

4

ALL I AM LORD
all I'll ever be
is all for you, Lord, take all of me.
All I have Lord, all I'll ever see
is all for you, Lord, take all of me.

*You are worthy, you are wonderful,
for your glory take all of me.
(Repeat)*

All I want Lord, all I'll ever need
is all of you, Lord, in all of me.
All I know Lord, all that I can see
is all your mercy over all of me.

4a Lord of all Peace

Blessed are you Lord of all peace.
From you comes peace;
open our lives to your peace,
open our dealings to your peace,
and fill our lives with your peace,
help us to live together in peace,
and worship you the God of all peace

5a Recognition of our calling

Almighty God, whose Son, Jesus Christ,
called the first disciples individually to follow
him, and who was recognised by Nathaniel
as 'the Son of God and the King of Israel' –
grant that we may recognise Christ's personal
calling to us and be ready to receive his
teaching and discipline,
through our Lord and Saviour Jesus Christ
who is alive and reigns with you
in the unity of the Holy Spirit,
one God, now and for ever. **Amen.**

5

ALL OF YOU
*is more than enough for all of me,
for every thirst and every need.
You satisfy me with your love,
and all I have in you is more than enough.*

You're my supply, my breath of life;
still more awesome than I know.
You're my reward, worth living for;
still more awesome than I know.

You're my sacrifice of greatest price;
still more awesome than I know.
You're my coming King, you are everything;
still more awesome than I know.

More than all I want, more than all I need,
you are more than enough for me.
More than all I know, more than all I can,
you are more than enough.

6

A LOVE SO AMAZING
has come to save me,
and this love changes everything.
Father, you found me, your goodness surrounds me;
I'm yours for eternity.

*And you will always be the King on the throne,
now your praise will always be on my tongue,
no one else could do the things
that you've done in my life.*

Your ways are faithful, your works are beautiful,
your word sets the captives free.
Your hand upon me heals and restores me,
your grace fills my every need.

*And you will always be the King on the throne,
now your praise will always be on my tongue,
no one else could do the things
that you've done in my life.*

*There's no greater love that's ever been shown,
and your song in me just has to be sung,
no one else could do the things
that you've done in my life.*

You said, if I follow you;
I'll know the truth and do the things you do.
Yours is the kingdom and the power,
for ever, Lord, you'll always be my God.

6a Lord of love

Lord you made us in love
and made us for love,
receive the love of your children.

7

A LOVE SO UNDESERVED

a gift that's free you lavish on me.
A peace I could not earn
and mercy for the freedom of my soul.

That's what's so amazing about your grace,
that's what's so amazing about your grace.
Lord, every day you pour on me
your blessings of eternity
and that's what's so amazing about your grace.

Forgiveness runs so deep
within your heart of loving kindness;
and should a soul forget
the cross of Christ reminds us every day.

Freely, I've received, now freely to give (x3)
give my life to you...

8

AMAZING GRACE

how sweet the sound
that saved a wretch like me;
I once was lost, but now am found,
was blind, but now I see.

Amazing love has come to me.
I lift up my voice to the heavens,
lift up my hands to the King,
and I cry 'hosanna, hosanna in the highest.'
Jesus my Lord is exalted far above every name,
and I cry 'hosanna, hosanna in the highest.'

'Twas grace that taught my heart to fear,
and grace my fears relieved;
how precious did that grace appear,
the hour I first believed!

The Lord has promised good to me,
his word my hope secures;
he will my shield and portion be
as long as life endures.

When we've been there a thousand years,
bright shining as the sun,
we've no less days to sing God's praise
than when we first begun.

8a Lord of all Grace

Lord of all grace embrace us
with that kiss from heaven
that awakens us to your love.
Open our hearts to your presence
and evoke within us awe
and wonder at your majesty and mystery.
Shine upon our lives that we might know the
warmth of your comfort and strength.
God of grace have mercy upon us.

9

AMAZING GRACE

how sweet the sound
that saved a wretch like me;
I once was lost, but now am found,
was blind, but now I see.

'Twas grace that taught my heart to fear,
and grace my fears relieved;
how precious did that grace appear,
the hour I first believed!

Through many dangers, toils and snares
I have already come;
'tis grace that brought me safe thus far,
and grace will lead me home.

The Lord has promised good to me,
his word my hope secures;
he will my shield and portion be
as long as life endures.

Yes, when this heart and flesh shall fail,
and mortal life shall cease,
I shall possess within the veil
a life of joy and peace.

When we've been there a thousand years,
bright shining as the sun,
we've no less days to sing God's praise
than when we first begun.

10
A MOUTH TO SING

a hand to raise,
feet to dance and give you praise
is what you've given, Lord, to me.
With a shout I will proclaim:
I have never been the same
since your love has captured me.

Thank you, Lord, for what you've done,
giving me a brand new life.

This is the day, that you, the Lord have made.
I will rejoice, and be glad in it.
This is the day, that you, the Lord have made,
I will rejoice and be glad;
I will rejoice and be glad.

...I will rejoice and be glad.
This is the day!

Dean Fearon
Copyright © Dean Fearon 2002 Nu Dymention

11
AS HIGH AS THE HEAVENS

are above the earth,
so high are your ways to mine.
Ways so perfect, they never fail me,
I know you are good all the time!

And through the storm, yet I will praise you.
Despite it all, yet I will sing.
Through good or bad, yet I will worship,
for you remain the same King of kings.

You are the voice of hope,
the anchor of my soul.
Where there seems to be no way,
you make it possible.
You are the Prince of peace amidst adversity.
My lips will shout for joy to you the most high.

You were the one before time began;
there's nothing beyond your control.
My confidence, my assurance rest
in your unchanging word!

And through the storm...

Lara Martin. Copyright © 2002 Thankyou Music
adm. UK & Europe by Kingsway Music. Used by permission.

12
AS IF YOU WERE NOT THERE

the skies ignite and thunder,
rivers tear their banks asunder,
thieves and nature storm and plunder;
all beware as if you were not there.

As if you were not there,
famine and flood together
usher death, disease and terror;
stricken mothers wonder whether
God heeds prayer, as if you were not there.

As if you were not there,
we televise the dying,
watch the helpless victims crying,
salve our consciences by sighing,
'Life's unfair!' as if you were not there.

As if you were not there,
your Son, when faith defied him,
faced a crowd which crucified him,
leaving friends who had denied him in despair,
as if you were not there.

Because he rose again
and showed God's love is vaster
than the ultimate disaster,
we entreat you now to master
strife and pain, because he rose again.

John L Bell & Graham Maule
Copyright © 1989, 1996, WGRG, The Iona Community

13a Jesus welcomes and includes people

Gracious God, through your Son
you lead us now to worship you
in spirit and in truth
and through him you offer us
the water of eternal life.
So wash away all our imperfections,
cleanse and heal our past hurts,
refresh dry minds and parched spirits
and quench our thirst with your living water
that flows to all from your life-giving fountain.
By the grace of our Saviour Jesus Christ
who is alive and reigns with you
in the unity of the Holy Spirit,
one God, now and for ever.

Amen.

Copyright © 2004 Marie Birkinshaw

13
AS WE GATHER FATHER SEAL US

in the love that knows no fear.
Draw us, heal us, reconcile us,
may there be a place of refuge here.

Who share one living bread
one Father's love,
one Saviour's grace, one Spirit's breath;
one holy communion.

No more outcasts,
no more strangers,
all dividing walls are down.
Here is love that redefines us,
dignifies the least and lowest one.

Source of joy, belonging, friendship,
form your family likeness here.
Father, Son and Holy Spirit,
that the world may know our God is near.

14
AT THE FOOT OF THE CROSS

where grace and suffering meet,
you have shown me your love
through the judgment you received.

And you've won my heart,
yes you've won my heart.

*Now I can trade these ashes in for beauty
and wear forgiveness like a crown.
Coming to kiss the feet of mercy,
I lay every burden down,
at the foot of the cross.*

At the foot of the cross
where I am made complete,
you have given me life
through the death you bore for me.

14a Collect for Good Friday

Almighty Father,
look with mercy on this your family
for which our Lord Jesus Christ was content
to be betrayed
and given up into the hands of sinners
and to suffer death upon the cross
who is alive and glorified with you and the
Holy Spirit,
one God, now and for ever.
Amen

15a Rejoicing in God
Luke 1: 46–47

My soul glorifies the Lord
and my spirit rejoices in God my Saviour.

15
AWAKE MY SOUL

rise up from your sleeping;
do not slumber or sleep anymore.
Raise your weary head to a new day;
lift your shout,
let your voice be heard.

Rocks will cry out if we are silent;
trees will clap their hands and rejoice.
The mighty ocean roars with a new song.
Mountains bow down to honour your name.

*Rise up, my soul, and sing.
Rise up, my soul, and sing.
Rise up, my soul, and give glory to the Lord.
(Repeat)*

Let the song of a bride in blooming
thunder clap through the heavens above.
Rising up in true adoration,
arise and shine for your light has come.

*I don't want to sleep anymore,
but I'll awake the dawn with singing.
Hear this crying heart of mine,
as I lift up my song.
(Repeat)*

Lift it up, lift it up, lift it up.

Rise up my soul and sing...

16
AWAKE, AWAKE

to this new day,
come, see this glorious morning.
Awake, awake, put on your strength,
put on your glorious clothing.
Stand up, stand up, stand up, stand up.

Shake yourself from the dust, arise. (x3)
Arise!

Awake, awake, awake new song,
come join the beautiful rhythm.
Awake, awake, awake the dawn,
come climb the beautiful mountain.
Stand up, stand up, stand up, stand up.

Break the chains off your neck, arise. (x3)
Arise!

17
A WORD IS SPOKEN

by the One;
'Let there be light' and worlds are born:
all creation comes to life at his command.
By your promise we're sustained,
the seedtime harvest shall remain,
our Creator's promises shall never fail.
You're the mighty world-creating God,
(whose glory cannot fade)
you're the promise-keeping God.

So say the word
that brought the universe to light.
Say the word
that put the powers of hell to flight.
Say the word to make me whole
that both wounds and heals my soul,
say the word.

But this creation fades away,
we wither, perish, fall, decay,
only his word remains for ever.
Planted in the humble heart,
a new creation makes the start,
gloriously growing to eternity.
You're the gracious, re-creating God,
(whose people will not fade)
you're the promise keeping God.

So say the word...

Let your Spirit cut deep into my soul,
turn a rebel heart into your home
a new creation, a holy nation to your praise!

Say the word (Repeat)

Steve James
Copyright © Steve James/Jubilee Hymns. Used by permission.

17a The Creator
Genesis 1: 1

In the beginning God created
the heavens and the earth.

18
BEFRIENDED

befriended by the King above all kings.
Surrendered, surrendered
to the friend above all friends.

Invited, invited, deep into this mystery.
Delighted, delighted
by the wonders I have seen.

This will be my story, this will be my song;
you'll always be my Saviour,
Jesus, you will always have my heart.

Astounded, astounded
that your gospel beckoned me.
Surrounded, surrounded
but I've never been so free.

Determined, determined
now to live this life for you.
You're so worthy, my greatest gift
would be the least you're due.

Matt Redman. Copyright © 2002 Thankyou Music
adm. UK & Europe by Kingsway Music. Used by permission

19
BE LIFTED UP, BE LIFTED UP.

As we bow down be lifted up.
(Repeat)

Let the heavens rejoice, let the nations be glad.
Let the whole earth tremble for you are God.

Come and worship the Lord
in the beauty of holiness.
As we bow down, be lifted up. (x2)

Paul Oakley. Copyright © 2001 Thankyou Music
adm. UK & Europe by Kingsway Music. Used by permission

19a From everlasting to everlasting
From 1 Chron 29 10–13

Praise be to you, O Lord,
God of our Father Israel
From everlasting to everlasting

Yours, O Lord, is the greatness
and the power and the glory
From everlasting to everlasting

Yours, O Lord, is the majesty
and the splendour,
for everything in heaven and earth is yours
From everlasting to everlasting

Yours O Lord is the Kingdom,
you are exalted as head over all
From everlasting to everlasting

Wealth and honour come from you,
you are the ruler of all things
From everlasting to everlasting

In your hands are strength and power
to exalt and give strength to all.
Now our God we give you thanks
and praise your glorious name
From everlasting to everlasting. Amen

20

BLESSED BE YOUR NAME

in the land that is plentiful
where your streams of abundance flow;
blessed be your name.

And blessed be your name
when I'm found in the desert place,
though I walk through the wilderness,
blessed be your name.

Every blessing you pour out I'll turn back to praise.
When the darkness closes in, Lord, still I will say:
'Blessed be the name of the Lord,
blessed be your name.
Blessed be the name of the Lord,
blessed be your glorious name.'

Blessed be your name
when the sun's shining down on me,
when the world's 'all as it should be';
blessed be your name.

And blessed be your name
on the road marked with suffering,
though there's pain in the offering;
blessed be your name.

You give and take away, you give and take away.
My heart will choose to say,
'Lord, blessed be your name.'

20a Help from the Lord
From Psalm 73

I am always with you;
you hold me by my right hand.
You guide me with your counsel,
and afterwards you will take me into glory.
Whom have I in heaven but you?
And earth has nothing I desire besides you.
My flesh and my heart may fail,
but God is the strength of my heart
and my portion for ever.

As for me, it is good to be near God.
I have made the Sovereign Lord my refuge;
I will tell of all your deeds.

21

CHRIST BE BEFORE ME

Christ be beside me,
Christ be all around.

22

CHRIST'S IS THE WORLD

in which we move,
Christ's are the folk we're summoned to love,
Christ's is the voice that calls us to care,
and Christ is the one who meets us here.

To the lost Christ shows his face,
to the unloved he gives his embrace,
to those who cry in pain or disgrace,
Christ makes, with his friends, a touching place.

Feel for the people we most avoid
strange, or bereaved, or never employed.
Feel for the women and feel for the men
who fear that their living is all in vain.

Feel for the parents who've lost their child,
feel for the women whom men have defiled,
feel for the baby for whom there's no breast
and feel for the weary who find no rest.

Feel for the lives by life confused,
riddled with doubt, in loving abused.
Feel for the lonely heart, conscious of sin,
which longs to be pure but fears to begin.

22a Your presence

You, Lord, are with us in this place
Your presence fills it
Your presence is peace

You, Lord, are with us in this place
Your presence fills it
Your presence awakens joy

You, Lord, are with us in this place
Your presence fills it
Your presence deepens trust

You, Lord, are with us in this place
Your presence fills it
Your presence brings hope

23a Praise the Lord
Psalm 150: 6

Let everything that has breath praise the Lord
Praise the Lord

23
COME ON EVERYBODY

let's praise his name!
Put your hands together and let's give him praise!
His love endures forever; it will never change,
and as he alone is worthy, we will praise his name.

I want to thank you for your goodness
as I look back on my life.
How you've showered me with blessings,
rescued me from strife.
I want to thank you for how you're there for me,
care for me:
my soul rejoices when I think of your great love!

My soul rejoices! (When I think of all he's done)
My soul rejoices! (How he gave his only Son)
My soul rejoices! (Every minute of every day)
My soul rejoices! (Cos he took my sin away!)

I want to thank you for your faithfulness
that reaches to the sky,
how your hand has been upon me
through the years gone by.
I want to thank you for how you walk with me,
talk with me,
my soul rejoices when I think of your great love!

Pete & Nicki Sims
Copyright © 2003 Kairos Music

24
COME PRAISE THE LORD

he is life in all it's fullness;
will you lift your voice?
Come, praise the Lord,
he is light that shatters darkness;
we have come to rejoice.

All around the world he is calling
people who would take up his call
and follow him.

Every breath be praise,
every heart be raised
to the King of all creation.
Every breath be praise,
every heart be raised
to the Lord of all.

Come, praise the Lord,
he is love that welcomes sinners;
will you give your life?
Come, praise the Lord,
he is great above all others;
all his ways are right.

Keith Getty & Kristyn Lennox. Copyright © 2002 Thankyou Music
adm. UK & Europe by Kingsway Music. Used by permission

24a Songs of Joy
Psalm 65: 8

Those living far away fear your wonders;
where morning dawns and evening fades
you call forth songs of joy

25
COME, WOUNDED HEALER

your sufferings reveal –
the scars you accepted,
our anguish to heal.
Your wounds bring such comfort
in body and soul
to all who bear torment
and yearn to be whole.

Come, hated Lover, and gather us near,
your welcome, your teaching,
your challenge to hear:
where scorn and abuse
cause rejection and pain,
your loving acceptance
makes hope live again!

Come, broken Victor,
condemned to a cross –
how great are the treasures
we gain from your loss!
Your willing agreement
to share in our strife
transforms our despair
into fulness of life.

Martin E Leckebusch. Copyright © 2000 Kevin Mayhew Ltd

26
CROSS OF JESUS, CROSS OF SORROW

where our sinfulness was laid.
Perfect love on you was broken
as the way to God was paved.
Cross of love – the scar of heaven,
cross of love – that heals my soul.
Let me not forget such mercy,
let me give the life I owe.

O what language shall I borrow,
as I praise you faithful friend.
How for us you bore our suffering,
in your love which has no end.
Died that I might be forgiven
by a power not my own.
With his glory set before me,
cross of Jesus lead me home.

Keith Getty & Kristyn Lennox. Copyright © 2003 Thankyou Music
adm. UK & Europe by Kingsway Music. Used by permission

27
CROWN OF GLORY, CROWN OF THORNS

Saviour of the world was born;
to die for us in sacrifice,
and rise and wear the crown of life.

Prince of peace, a pauper came
with riches sure enough,
to light the true, eternal flame:
the Father's heart of love.
Son of God and Son of man,
you walked among us here,
you knew the fragile hearts we are,
you shared our joy and tears.

King of love, you bore our sin
that nailed you to the cross;
tears of God, shed to reclaim
the broken and the lost.
Lord of light from darkness shone
in power to rise again,
for death has no dominion now,
the King of life shall reign.

God with us, Emmanuel
the Shepherd and the Lamb;
from now until eternity
your faithfulness will stand.
Hallelujah! Living God,
our hope is in your name:
by your grace we come to you:
renew our faith again.

28
DANCE, DANCE

everybody dance,
everybody sing, for joy is in this place now.
(Repeat)

Everybody dance now. (Repeat)

Amazing grace how sweet the sound
to save a wretch like me;
I once was lost but now I'm found,
was blind but now I see.

Shout, shout everybody shout,
everybody scream, for joy is in this place now.
(Repeat)

Yeah, joy is in this place now. (Repeat)

29
EVERLASTING GOD

the years go by but you're unchanging.
In this fragile world,
you are the only firm foundation.

Always loving, always true,
always merciful and good, so good.

Yesterday, today and forever,
you are the same, you never change.
Yesterday, today and forever,
you are faithful and we will trust in you.

Uncreated One,
you have no end and no beginning.
Earthly powers fade,
but there is no end to your kingdom.

Always loving...

Yesterday, today and forever...

Yahweh, God unchanging.
Yahweh, firm foundation.
(Repeat)

Yesterday, today and forever...

30
EVERLASTING, EVER TRUE

all creation sings to you.
Ever faithful, living Lord,
let the sound of praise be heard.

Jesus, you are
all that I am living for
and all that I believe is in you.
Jesus, all that I am living for
and all that I believe is in you.

Never changing, awesome God.
Sing the glory of the Lord.
Ever loving, holy One,
I will praise what you have done.

31
FAITHFUL AND TRUE

he is brother and friend,
the kindness and love of God.
Lord over all, he is righteous and just,
the wonderful Son of God.
(Repeat)

continued over...

This is my Jesus – victorious name!
Only in Jesus I stand forgiv'n.
The Lord of glory, Saviour of the world
this is my Jesus, my God.

Lamb sacrificed; he's the redeeming One,
worthy of all my praise.
King above all; he is full of love's power,
the glorious Son of God.

(Additional chorus):
This is my Jesus – victorious name!
only in you Lord I stand forgiv'n.
The Lord of glory, Saviour of the world,
you are my Jesus, my God.

32
FATHER, LET ME DEDICATE

all this life to thee,
in whatever worldly state thou wilt have me be.
Not from sorrow, pain or care
freedom dare I claim;
this alone shall be my prayer: glorify thy name.

Be glorified in me, be glorified.
Be glorified in me, be glorified.

Can a child presume to choose
where or how to live?
Can a father's love refuse all the best to give?
Let my glad heart, while it sings,
thee in all proclaim,
and, whatever the future brings, glorify thy name.

32a Jesus shows us Mercy and Grace

Jesus came to a world fraught with
condemnation and blame, where he alone
stood pure and without sin.
And still today he is ready to greet repentant
sinners without condemnation.
He shows us mercy and grace.
He offers us an opportunity to change
and to be made whole.
So let us examine ourselves as we come before
Almighty God in worship and, through
confession and thanksgiving, may we find
renewal and hope.

33
FATHER WE HAVE SINNED

in word, and deed, and thought;
through ignorance, through weakness,
through deliberate fault.
We've sinned against our neighbours
and against you, Lord,
yet we are truly sorry,
and we turn to you once more.

Father of the nations, you who bless the poor,
we're servants of the endless
want and drive for more.
We've made our greed a virtue
while the children starve;
come, change our joy to sorrow,
till our lives reflect your heart.

34
FATHER, YOUR LOVE

is a faithful love,
enduring and never failing love.
Throughout the ages, steady and true,
and the dawn of each day brings your mercies new.
And I will put my trust in you,
Father, your love is faithful.

So keep me in your love today,
take my hand and lead the way,
and let my words and life convey,
Father, your love is faithful.

Great is your faithfulness (x3)
my God and Father.

34a Circle me Lord

Circle me Lord;
keep protection near and danger afar.
Circle me Lord;
keep hope within and despair without.
Circle me Lord;
keep love within and evil out.
Circle me Lord;
keep pride without and humility within.
Circle me Lord;
keep peace within and fear removed.
The peace of all peace be ours this day. Amen.

35

FOR EVERY CHILD THAT STANDS ABUSED

for all the lonely and confused,
for those who suffer for the truth, hear our prayer.

For those who mourn the ones they knew,
who stand accused for loving you,
Lord we long to see you move; hear our prayer.

Hear our prayer (x4)

For all who bear the marks of hate,
who are wounded for your sake,
these are champions of the faith, hear our prayer.

Hear our prayer (x4)

For those who weep, for those who grieve;
for those in need we intercede.

Console the powerless and the weak,
the ones denied a right to speak;
bring your comfort and release, hear our prayer.

Hear our prayer (x4)

Dave Bilbrough. Copyright © 2003 Thankyou Music
adm. UK & Europe by Kingsway Music. Used by permission

35a Living with God
Psalm 61: 4

I long to dwell in your tent for ever
and take refuge in the shelter of your wings

36

FOR EVERY DISAPPOINTMENT

for every broken heart,
for every one in darkness; a light.

For every wounded person,
for every tired mind,
for hopeless situations; a hope.

The cross still stands, the cross still towers,
his blood still cleanses, eternally the same.

For everyone who's desperate,
for everyone who's lost,
for everyone who's fearful; a shelter.

For every painful question,
for everyone's regrets,
for every cry of 'Why God?'; an answer.

Grace and peace, mercy and joy
all undeserved, I bow down.

The cross still stands ...

(Instrumental verse)

And I bow down,
Lord, I run to the cross again.
I bow down, I bow down.

David Hind. Copyright © 2003 Alliance Media
Admin by CopyCare. Used by permission.

37

FOR THE GRACE OF GOD

that brings salvation
has come for everyone in every nation,
and it teaches us to say 'no' to all ungodliness.
And the peace of God beats all understanding,
renewing our minds, free from entangling,
and it teaches us to be still in all our busyness.

While we wait for the blessed hope,
for the glorious appearing
of our great God and Saviour.
While we wait we can rest assured
of the glorious appearing
of our great God and Saviour.

For the love of God beyond all measure,
pours into our hearts the joy of heaven,
and it teaches us to add faith
to see his kingdom come.
And the power of God at work within us
is greater than any force of evil,
and it teaches us to press in,
and to stand, stand strong.

Godfrey & Gill Birtill. Copyright © 2000 Whitefield Music UK
admin. CopyCare. Used by permission.

38

GIVE THANKS TO THE LORD

our God and King: his love endures forever.
For he is good, he is above all things.
His love endures forever.
Sing praise, sing praise.

With a mighty hand and an outstretched arm
his love endures forever.
For the life that's been reborn.
His love endures forever.
Sing praise, sing praise. (x2)

Forever, God is faithful, forever God is strong.
Forever God is with us, forever, forever.

From the rising to the setting sun
his love endures forever.
By the grace of God, we will carry on.
His love endures forever.
Sing praise, sing praise. (x2)

Chris Tomlin. Copyright © 2000 worshiptogether.com songs/
Six steps Music/Adm. by Kingsway Music
For the UK & Europe. Used by permission.

39

GLORY TO HIM

who has saved us,
and freed us from sin by his blood.
Jesus, the radiance of God,
the glory of the Father in us.

We crown you now with worship and honour,
King of kings, Lord of lords, there's no other.
Holy, holy God Almighty,
Jesus Lord of all.

You are high and lifted up, high and lifted up,
high and lifted up, Son of God.

Lara Martin & Mark Stevens. Copyright © 2002 Thankyou Music
adm. UK & Europe by Kingsway Music. Used by permission

40

GOD OF THE MOUNTAINS

God of the sea,
God of the heavens, of eternity.
God of the future, God of the past,
God of the present, God of all history.

Creation praise will thunder to you,
thunder to you, thunder to you.
Creation praise will thunder to you,
I'm lost in the wonder,
lost in the wonder of you.

Wisdom of ages, light in the dark,
home for the outcast, peace for the heart:
friend of the lonely, strength for oppressed,
voice of the voiceless, God of all liberty.

Sue Rinaldi, Caroline Bonnett & Steve Bassett
Copyright © 2001 Thankyou Music adm. UK & Europe
by Kingsway Music. Used by permission

41

GOD OF GRACE

amazing wonder, irresistible and free.
Oh the miracle of mercy;
Jesus reaches down to me.
God of grace, I stand in wonder,
as my God restores my soul:
his own blood has paid my ransom;
awesome cost to make me whole.

God of grace who loved and knew me
long before the world began;
sent my Saviour down from heaven:
perfect God and perfect man.
God of grace, I trust in Jesus
I'm accepted as his own.
Every day new grace sustains me,
as I lean on him alone.

God of grace, I stand astounded,
cleansed, forgiven and secure.
All my fears are now confounded
and my hope is ever sure.
God of grace, now crowned in glory,
where one day I'll see your face;
and forever I'll adore you
in your everlasting grace.

Keith Getty & Jonathan Rea
Copyright © 2003 Thankyou Music
adm. UK & Europe by Kingsway Music. Used by permission

42

GOOD AND GRACIOUS

attributes of a loving Father,
you're high and mighty,
but humble all the same.
You have made the heavens and the earth,
and you made us in your image, Lord.

Holy, holy, holy is the Lord Almighty
and we rejoice in you alone,
for you are worthy.
And you have given life to me,
and I love to worship at your feet,
and I love to love you just for who you are.

Death are hell are
now no longer things I fear because
you have saved me
and I'm grateful to the core.
I'm your child because of Jesus' blood,
and your Spirit leads me,
guides me, fills me.

Holy, holy, holy is the Lord Almighty
and we rejoice in you alone, for you are worthy.
And you have given life to me,
and I love to worship at your feet,
and I love to love you just for who you are.

I'm so grateful for the things
you have given me:
your love, your grace, your joy,
your peace and more.

Holy, holy, holy, holy.

Gareth Robinson. Copyright © 2001 Thankyou Music
adm. UK & Europe by Kingsway Music. Used by permission

42a Streams of Grace

Lord may the streams of your grace
flow through the dry deserts of our own hearts,
the barren wastelands of the church
and the parched wildernesses of your world.
In your mercy hear the cry of our hearts,
your church and the world. Amen

43
GRACE AND MERCY

wash over me,
cleanse my soul with your healing stream.
Here I stand with this prayer within my heart.
Take me deeper in the river
that flows with your love.

*Thank you, thank you,
oh what riches are mine in Christ Jesus.
Thank you, thank you,
your forgiveness is so undeserved.*

43a Come and see

As he did with the first disciples,
the Lord in his goodness and grace invites us
to 'Come and see,'
to set time aside to be with him.
So let us put away all that would distract and
let us be still in the presence of the Lord
as we prepare to worship God together.

44
GREAT AND WONDERFUL

are your deeds and works,
Lord God, the Almighty.
Just and true and righteous are all your ways,
ruler of the nations.
Who shall not fear and praise your name,
O Sovereign Lord?
For you alone, you are the holy One.
The world shall bow in worship
at your throne of grace,
your righteousness has been made manifest.

To him who reigns in majesty and to the Lamb,
to him who reigns in majesty and to the Lamb,
be blessing and honour and glory and might,
for ever and for ever;
be blessing and honour and glory and might,
for ever and for ever.

...Amen.

45
GREAT IS YOUR FAITHFULNESS

Great is your faithfulness.
You never change, you never fail, O God.

True are your promises. (x2)
You never change, you never fail, O God.

*So we raise up holy hands
to praise the holy One;
who was, and is, and is to come.*

Wide is your love and grace. (x2)
You never change, you never fail, O God.

You were, you are, you will always be. (x2)

46
HE IS GOOD

*he is faithful, he is kind.
He is patient, he is loving, he is wise.
He was willing to make the sacrifice
so we will come and worship with our lives.*

If you are weary,
there is rest here by his side.
If you are broken,
there is healing by his side.

If you are hungry,
there is truth here in his life.
If you are thirsty,
there is love here in his eyes.

Come let us adore him,
come let us bow down.
(Repeat)

*(Alternative chorus):
You are good, you are faithful, you are kind.
You are patient, you are loving, you are wise.
And you were willing to make the sacrifice
so we will come and worship with our lives.*

47
HEAR MY PRAYER, O LORD
from the ends of the earth I cry.
Your peace will lead me to
the rock that is higher than I.

For you have been my strength
in times of trouble,
a tower above my enemies.
And Lord, I will abide with you forever
in the shelter of your wings.

48
HERE I AM
humbled by your majesty,
covered by your grace so free.
Here I am, knowing I'm a sinful man,
covered by the blood of the Lamb.

Now I've found the greatest love of all is mine,
since you laid down your life, the greatest sacrifice.

Majesty, majesty.
Your grace has found me just as I am,
empty handed but alive in your hands.
Majesty, majesty.
Forever I am changed by your love,
in the presence of your majesty.

Here I am, humbled by the love that you give,
forgiven so that I can forgive.
Here I stand, knowing that I'm your desire,
sanctified by glory and fire.

Now I've found...

49
HERE I AM, MY GOD
I've come to seek your face;
I long to know you more in my life.
Here I am, my Lord, I want to meet with you;
I long to know your glory in this place.

My heart yearns for you, my soul thirsts for you.

'Cause you're my Rock,
you're my light, you're my hope,
you're my song in the night.
You're the air that I breathe;
you're the food my soul wants, my soul needs.

50
HIDE ME NOW
under your wings.
Cover me within your mighty hand.

When the oceans rise and thunders roar,
I will soar with you above the storm.
Father, you are King over the flood;
I will be still and know you are God.

Find rest, my soul, in Christ alone,
know his power in quietness and trust.

50a Lord be with ...

Lord be with ....
Surround them with your love
In waking and sleeping
In joy and in pain
In their waiting and longing
Enfold ... with your peace
Encircle ... with your protection
Embrace ... with your peace
Endue ... with your hope.

51
HOLY GOD
generations know your promises,
your covenant of love.
Lord of all, every promise made
you remain faithful to fulfil.
For your ways are holy,
and your name is worthy;
all honour and glory belong to you.

You are faithful, mighty, glorious,
awesome and victorious,
beautiful and wonderful, Lord.
Now our hearts are resolute;
our confidence is all in you,
everything is possible, O Lord, my Lord.

When troubles come, when life overwhelms,
you are Lord, you are in control.
I trust in you, for in my darkest day
you remain worthy of my praise!
For your ways are higher,
and your arm is stronger,
and your rest is sweeter than any other.

51a Wait for the Lord
Psalm 27: 13–14

Wait for the Lord;
be strong and take heart
and wait for the Lord.

52
HOLY, HOLY GOD ALMIGHTY
who was and is to come.
God of glory, you're so worthy,
all the saints bow down.

Holy is your name in all the earth.
Righteous are your ways, so merciful.
Everything you've done is just and true.
Holy, holy God are you. (x2)

All blessing, all honour belongs to you.
All power, all wisdom is yours.

52a The Easter anthems

Christ our Passover has been sacrificed for us,
so let us celebrate the feast not with the old
leaven of corruption and wickedness but with
the unleavened bread of sincerity and truth.
Christ once raised from the dead dies no
more; death has no more dominion over him.
In dying, he died to sin once for all; in living,
he lives to God.
See yourselves, therefore, as dead to sin and
alive to God in Jesus Christ our Lord.
Christ has been raised from the dead;
the first fruits of those who sleep.
For since by one man came death, by another
has come also the resurrection of the dead.
For as in Adam all die, even so in Christ shall
all be made alive.
Glory to the Father and to the Son and to the
Holy Spirit as it was it is and shall be forever.
Amen

53
HOLY ONE EXALTED FOREVER.
Holy One, he is the Lord.

Risen One, God's own Son,
victory won, death is defeated.

53a Jesus Christ is Lord
Philippians 2: 10–11

God exalted him to the highest place
and gave him the name that is above every name
that at the name of Jesus every knee should bow
in heaven and on earth and under the earth,
and every tongue confess that
Jesus Christ is Lord,
to the glory of God the Father.

54
HOW GOOD IT IS
to give thanks unto the Lord.
How good it is to sing his praises.
How good it is to give thanks unto the Lord,
singing sweet praises to the Lord.

Be thankful every boy and girl;
sing it out, be thankful everyone.
He's faithful to those who call upon his name,
Christ the Lord of all.

Be thankful every boy and girl
sing it out, be thankful every one.
He's faithful, he can make you clean
deep down inside,
no matter where you've been.

54a One thing I have asked of the Lord

One thing I have asked of the Lord,
this is what I seek:
that I may dwell in the house of the Lord
all the days of my life;
to behold the beauty of the Lord
and to seek him in his temple.

Leader: Who is it that you seek?
All: We seek the Lord our God.

Leader: Do you seek him with all your heart?
All: Amen. Lord, have mercy.

Leader: Do you seek him with all your soul?
All: Amen. Lord, have mercy.

Leader: Do you seek him with all your mind?
All: Amen. Lord, have mercy.

Leader: Do you seek him with all your strength?
All: Amen. Christ, have mercy.

55

I CAN ONLY IMAGINE

what it will be like when I walk by your side.
I can only imagine what my eyes will see
when your face is before me.

Surrounded by your glory, what will my heart feel?
Will I dance for you Jesus, or in awe of you be still?
Will I stand in your presence
or to my knees will I fall?
Will I sing hallelujah? Will I be able to speak at all?
I can only imagine, I can only imagine.

I can only imagine when that day comes
and I find myself standing in the Son.
I can only imagine when all I will do
is forever, forever worship you.
I can only imagine.

56

I HAVE BEEN CRUCIFIED WITH CHRIST

and the life I now live I live by faith.
I have been crucified with Christ,
and the Son of God willingly died for me.

And I no longer live,
but it's Christ who lives in me;
and I will reign with him,
it's Christ in me, the hope of glory (x2)

57

I HAVE NO-ONE IN HEAVEN BUT YOU

I want nothing on earth besides you,
for you alone are holy, Lord, you alone are holy.

I have no-one in heaven but you.
I want nothing on earth besides you,
for you alone are holy, Lord,
you alone are trustworthy.

So I will sing my praise to you,
for you are good, you are true.
No earthly thing compares to you,
always faithful, ever loving, mighty God.

And no-one gives me life like you do.
No-one gives me peace like you do.
No-one gives me grace like you do.
No-one gives me hope like you.

58

I KNEEL IN WONDER

then fall on my face
as my Maker hangs before me.
Created hands strike nails in today,
my human sin, his divine tears.

Your eyes watch over the whole of the earth,
yet I feel your gaze upon me.
Your storms of love sweep cities away,
yet my soul can sense your Spirit's breeze.

How does it feel,
to be ruler of all
and then subject to evil?
How does it feel,
to be strung up for all to see?

Will you teach me how I can follow this way,
how a love so large could fill me?
I get my life to give it away:
to live is Christ, but to die is gain.

59

I LIVE MY LIFE TO WORSHIP YOU

I spend my days serving you,
and now I come, I come.
I want to spend some time with you,
to steal away and be with you,
so now I come, I come.

Just to be with you,
just to know more of your love;
just to be with you, and to love you.

And here you know me,
and here you love me
and here I know you,
and here I love you.

60

MEN: I LOVE YOU WITH ALL OF MY HEART

Women: *I love you with all of my heart*
Men: *I love you with all of my mind*
Women: *I love you with all of my mind*
All: *I love you with all of my soul*
and all my strength;
you have won me Lord Almighty.

Forgiven I stand,
accepted before the Almighty;
totally free of all of my guilt and shame.
Now that I've found
the reason why I'm living
your joy fills my heart,
I yield you my life again.

Gracious and true
faithful are you, Almighty,
that you would show
and bring me to know your love.
You break through my blindness,
revealing to me such glory.
Where once I knew darkness
now is your beautiful light.

60a Christ as a light

Christ, as a light, illumine and guide me.
Christ, as a shield, overshadow me.
Christ under me, Christ over me,
Christ beside me, on my left and my right.
This day be within and without me,
lowly and meek, yet all-powerful.
Be in the heart of each to whom I speak;
in the mouth of each who speaks unto me.
This day be within and without me,
lowly and meek yet all-powerful.
Christ as a light; Christ as a shield;
Christ beside me on my left and my right.

61a Every spiritual blessing
Ephesians 1: 3

Praise be to the God and Father
of our Lord Jesus Christ,
who has blessed us in the heavenly realms
with every spiritual blessing in Christ.

61
I'M MAKING MELODY
IN MY HEART TO YOU

I'm making melody in my heart to you.
Pouring out your praise with everything within.

I'm making melody in my heart to you.
I'm making melody in my heart to you.
Yours will always be the song I love to sing.

How can hearts not love your name?
How can souls not sing your praise?
Jesus, you've put music in my soul.

62
I'M TRADING MY SORROWS

I'm trading my shame.
I'm laying them down
for the joy of the Lord.

I'm trading my sickness,
I'm trading my pain.
I'm laying them down
for the joy of the Lord.

I say: 'yes Lord, yes Lord, yes yes Lord
yes Lord, yes Lord, yes yes Lord
yes Lord, yes Lord, yes yes Lord
amen.'

I am pressed but not crushed,
persecuted not abandoned,
struck down but not destroyed.
I am blessed beyond the curse
for his promise will endure:
that his joy's gonna be my strength.

Though the sorrow may last for the night,
his joy comes with the morning.

63
IN CHRIST ALONE MY HOPE IS FOUND

he is my light, my strength, my song;
this cornerstone, this solid ground,
firm through the fiercest drought and storm.
What heights of love, what depths of peace,
when fears are stilled, when strivings cease!
My comforter, my all in all,
here in the love of Christ I stand.

In Christ alone! – who took on flesh,
fulness of God in helpless babe!
This gift of love and righteousness,
scorned by the ones he came to save.
Till on that cross as Jesus died,
the wrath of God was satisfied –
for every sin on him was laid;
here in the death of Christ I live.

There in the ground his body lay,
light of the world by darkness slain
then bursting forth in glorious day
up from the grave he rose again!

continued over...

And as he stands in victory
sin's curse has lost its grip on me;
for I am his and he is mine –
bought with the precious blood of Christ.

No guilt in life, no fear in death,
this is the power of Christ in me;
from life's first cry to final breath,
Jesus commands my destiny.
No power of hell, no scheme of man,
can ever pluck me from his hand;
till he returns or calls me home,
here in the power of Christ I'll stand!

*Keith Getty & Stuart Townend. Copyright © 2001 Thankyou Music
adm. UK & Europe by Kingsway Music. Used by permission*

63a Saved by Grace
Ephesians 2: 8–10

It is by grace you have been saved,
through faith – and this not from yourselves,
it is the gift of God – not by works,
so that no-one can boast.
For we are God's workmanship,
created in Christ Jesus to do good works,
which God prepared in advance for us to do.

64
IN EVERY DAY THAT DAWNS
I see the light of your splendour around me;
and ev'rywhere I turn,
I know the gift of your favour upon me.
What can I do but give you glory, Lord?
Ev'rything good has come from you.

*I'm grateful for the air I breathe,
I'm so thankful for this life I live,
for the mercies that you pour on me,
and the blessings that meet ev'ry need.
And the grace that is changing me
from a hopeless case to a child that's free,
free to give you praise,
for in ev'rything I know you love me.
I know you love me.*

Through all that I have known,
I have been held in the shelter of your hand;
and as my life unfolds,
you are revealing the wisdom
of your sovereign plan.
There are no shadows in your faithfulness,
there are no limits to your love.

*Kate Simmonds & Stuart Townend. Copyright © 2001 Thankyou Music
adm. UK & Europe by Kingsway Music. Used by permission*

65
INTO THE CENTRE
of the fallen ages,
you moved among us with uncommon grace;
and you know we're thirsty, weary and poor,
you know.

You are acquainted with our suffering,
you are familiar with our silent pain;
and you know we're searching, with every prayer,
you know the brokenness we have to bear.

*You know the hunger of our generation,
you know the lies that we've been captive of,
you know we're longing for a revelation,
you know.*

Each day we rise with hearts that hope again,
another page we hope to find you in
and you know we're searching with every prayer,
you know we're asking; 'Father, are you there?'

*Dan Wilt & Bruce Ellis. Copyright © 2003 Vineyard Songs Canada
admin. CopyCare. Used by permission.*

65a Bread of heaven

Jesus is the bread of heaven for eternal life.
In this time of worship, may we find his
sustenance and strength,
and by the leading of the Holy Spirit,
may we come ready to receive from Father God.
Let our hearts and minds be resolved to offer
him thanks and praise
through Christ our Lord.
Amen.

Copyright © 2004 Marie Birkinshaw

66
I REJOICED WHEN THEY SAID TO ME
*let us go, let us go
to the house of the Lord.*

Our feet are standing in your gates,
your gathered people now the place,
a living temple built to praise you.

These gates, by Christ, held open wide;
his sacrifice, the way prescribed,
we enter in, his praises singing.

The walls have now been broken;
brought near by Jesus' blood.
The temple he is building
shall stand for ever more.

I rejoiced when...

Sure in the promises of him,
let there be grace and peace within;
reflect the beauty of the Saviour!

Where every nation, tribe and tongue
will gather round your throne as one,
in unity his praises singing.

From glory into glory,
in heaven we take our place,
we cast our crowns before him
in wonder, love and praise.

I rejoiced when...

Rejoice in the Lord.

66a Blessing for the journey

May the peace of the Lord Christ go with you
wherever he may send you.
May he guide you through the wilderness,
protect you through the storm.
May he bring you home rejoicing
at the wonders he has shown you.
May he bring you home rejoicing
once again into our doors.

67a The God who made the world
Acts 17: 24–28

The God who made the world and everything
in it is the Lord of heaven and earth and does
not live in temples built by hands.

And he is not served by human hands, as if he
needed anything, because he himself gives all
men life and breath and everything else.

From one man he made every nation of men,
that they should inhabit the whole earth;
and he determined the times set for them and
the exact places where they should live.

God did this so that men would seek him
and perhaps reach out for him and find him,
though he is not far from each one of us.

For in him we live and move and have our
being.

67
IT IS BY YOUR MIGHTY POWER
that we live and that we move.
It is by your mighty power that we breathe.
And in the name of Jesus risen,
by the Holy Spirit given,
it is by your mighty power we believe.

*And you're God above all rule and reign
and all authority.
Yet you have come to live in us,
and it is by your mighty power we believe.*

You enable us to walk even in the darkest night,
and you equip us to be bearers of your life.
We are salt and we are light,
we're already in the fight,
but it is by your mighty power that we stand.

When the clouds are pushed aside,
and we move into that place
where all the nations of the world
will throw their crowns,
and as we gaze upon your face,
we will sing for endless days,
that it's by your mighty power that we've come.

68
I WAIT FOR THE LORD
my soul waits;
and in his word I put my hope.
(Repeat)

*My soul waits for the Lord,
more than watchmen wait for morning. (Repeat)*

I hope in the Lord, I call on him,
for with the Lord is unfailing love.
I cry to the Lord, 'hear my voice,
I call you from the depths of my soul'.

My soul waits for the Lord...

If you, Lord, remembered my sin,
I could not stand before you now.
I hold up my head to face you, Lord;
I stand forgiven and restored.

*But search me, search my heart
for offensive ways within me.
O search me, lead me on
in your righteous ways eternal.*

I wait for the Lord...

69
I WANT TO KNOW

your pleasing and perfect will for me,
so renew my mind.
Open my eyes so I can see
the wonderful things you have for me,
amazing love.

Draw me nearer to you, Lord,
that I might know you more, faithful God.
Only you can satisfy:
breathe on me your breath of life,
'cause all I want to do is be
a living sacrifice for you.

And if I see you, I will know you.
And if I know you, then I will love like you.

70
I WORSHIP YOU

I honour you:
pouring out my love to you,
laying down my all for you,
surrendering my life to you;
this is what I live to do.

On the altar of the Lord,
we offer up our lives;
in worship to the most high God
we bring our sacrifice.

I worship you, I honour you ...

When I think of your great love,
the scars you bore for me:
on the cross you took my shame,
and gave me freedom through your name.

I worship you, I honour you.
I worship you, I honour you.

71
I WILL RETURN TO YOU

and say I am not fit to be your slave,
for I have sinned and turned away.
My journey home is filled with fear
of what I'll find when I draw near.
Is there a welcome for me here?

Then running towards me, a beautiful sight;
a Father who loves his own.
He's standing before me, exploding with life,
so I offer up my own.

Into your open arms, into your open arms,
into your open arms I throw myself.
Into your open arms, into your open arms,
into your open arms, your arms of saving grace.

You know how faithfully I've served,
all your commands I have observed,
yet he receives what I deserve.
Have I forgotten where I stand,
taken for granted who I am,
a child held in my father's hands?

Come to the table and join in the feast,
where joy and grace abound.
For once I was dead, but now I'm alive,
I was lost, but now I'm found.

71a Opening prayer for Easter Sunday

The night has passed and the day lies open
before us;
let us pray with one heart and mind;

(Silence may be kept)

As we rejoice in the gift of this new day
this resurrection Sunday,
so may the light of your presence, O God
set our hearts on fire with love for you,
now and for ever
Amen

72
JESUS CHRIST, YOU ARE THE SON OF GOD

holy One, you gave everything
to become like one of us.
Heaven's Son came to earth,
showed a selfless way to live and how to love.

On my knees I will fall
in surrender to your love.
(Repeat)

You obeyed God's plan to the very end, holy One,
became the sacrifice that would
show us the Father's love.
You came to die to give us life,
and now I give myself to you the humble King.

One day all the world will see you,
one day all the world will see
all creation kneel before you, all creation sing.

73
JESUS, BE THE CENTRE
be my source, be my light, Jesus.

Jesus, be the centre,
be my hope, be my song, Jesus.

Be the fire in my heart,
be the wind in these sails,
be the reason that I live; Jesus, Jesus.

Jesus, be my vision,
be my path, be my guide, Jesus.

(Repeat verse 1)

Michael Frye. Copyright © 1999 Vineyard Songs (UK/Eire)
admin. by CopyCare. Used by permission.

73a The Lord's prayer
Based on Matthew 6: 9–13

As our Saviour taught us, so we pray

Our Father in heaven,
hallowed be your name,
your kingdom come,
your will be done,
on earth as in heaven.
Give us today our daily bread.
Forgive us our sins
as we forgive those who sin against us.
Lead us not into temptation
but deliver us from evil.
For the kingdom, the power,
and the glory are yours
now and for ever. Amen.

From Common Worship: Services and Prayers for the Church of England.
Copyright © The Archbishops' Council 2000

74
JESUS, I'VE FORGOTTEN
the words that you have spoken;
promises that burned within my heart
have now grown dim;
with a doubting heart I follow
the paths of earthly wisdom;
forgive me for my unbelief, renew the fire again.

Lord have mercy, Christ have mercy,
Lord have mercy on me.
(Repeat)

I have built an altar where I worship things of man;
I have taken journeys
that have drawn me far from you;
so now I am returning to your mercies ever flowing;
pardon my transgressions, help me love you again.

I have longed to know you
and all your tender mercies,
like a river of forgiveness ever flowing without end.
So I bow my heart before you
in the goodness of your presence,
your grace forever shining
like a beacon in the night.

Steve Merkel
Copyright © 2000 Integrity's Hosanna! Music/Sovereign Music UK

75
JESUS IS LORD
the cry that echoes through creation:
resplendent power, eternal word, our rock,
the Son of God –
the King whose glory fills the heavens,
yet bids us come to taste this living bread.

Jesus is Lord, whose word sustains
the stars and planets,
yet in his wisdom laid aside his crown.
Jesus the man, who washed our feet,
who bore our suffering,
became a curse to bring salvation's plan.

Jesus is Lord – the tomb is gloriously empty!
Not even death could crush this King of love!
The price is paid – the chains are loosed
and we're forgiven,
and we can run into the arms of God.

'Jesus is Lord' a shout of joy, a cry of anguish,
as he returns and every knee bows low
then every eye and every heart will see his glory
the judge of all will take his children home.

Keith Getty & Stuart Townend. Copyright © 2003 Thankyou Music
adm. UK & Europe by Kingsway Music. Used by permission

76
JESUS, MELT MY COLD HEART
break my stony emotions.
Cos I've been playing with the waves
when I should be swimming in the ocean.

Take me deeper, show me more.
It's all or nothing,
I give you everything, my Lord.

Jesus, show your mercy,
I'm so sorry for waiting,
I should be running to your heart,
but I know I've been hesitating.

Caroline Bonnett & Steve Bassett. Copyright © 2001 Thankyou Music
adm. UK & Europe by Kingsway Music. Used by permission

77
JESUS, MY PASSION IN LIFE
is to know you.
May all other goals bow down to this
journey of loving you more.

Jesus, you've showered your goodness on me,
given your gifts so freely.
But there's one thing I'm longing for.

Hear my heart's cry,
and my prayer for this life.

Above all else, above all else,
above all else give me yourself.

Vicky Beeching
Copyright © 2001 Vineyard Songs (UK/Eire) admin. by CopyCare

78
JESUS, THE VERY THOUGHT OF THEE
with sweetness fills the breast,
but sweeter far thy face to see,
and in thy presence rest.
Nor voice can sing, nor heart can frame,
nor can the memory find
a sweeter sound than thy blessed name,
O, Saviour of mankind.

O hope of every contrite heart,
O joy of all the meek,
to those who fall, how kind thou art,
how good to those who seek!
But what to those who find?
Ah this, nor tongue nor pen can show,
the love of Jesus, what it is –
none but his loved ones know.

Jesus, thy mercies are untold
through each returning day;
thy love exceeds a thousandfold
whatever we can say.
Jesus, our only joy be thou,
as thou our prize wilt be;
Jesus, be thou our glory now,
and through eternity.

Bernard of Clairvaux (1091-1153)
tr. Edward Caswall (1814-1878)

78a Glory to the Lamb
Revelation 5: 13

To him who sits on the throne and to the Lamb
be praise and honour and glory and power,
for ever and ever!
Amen

79
JESUS YOU ALONE
must be my first love, my first love.
The secret place and highest praise
shall be yours, shall be yours.

To your throne I'll bring devotion,
may it be the sweetest sound:
Lord, this heart is reaching for you now.

So I'll set my sights upon you,
set my life upon your praise;
never looking to another way.
You alone will be my passion,
Jesus, you will be my song:
you will find me longing after you.

Day and night I lift my eyes
to seek you, to seek you.
Hungry for a glimpse of you
in glory, in glory.

Tim Hughes. Copyright © 1999 Thankyou Music
adm. UK & Europe by Kingsway Music. Used by permission

80
KING OF THE AGES
history's pages point to you.
Ancient of Days, all of your ways
show your wonders.
Jehovah Jireh, our awesome provider and healer,
author of time, be glorified as we worship.

Father to nations, forever patient and faithful.
To each generation
you show compassion and mercy.
Jehovah Nissi, our sovereign protector and fortress,
Lord of all time be glorified as we worship.

All you have done
tells of your greatness, tells of your worth.
The works of your hands display your majesty.
All you have done
shows us your goodness, shows us your abundance.
The works of your hands reveal your glory.

Eoghan Heaslip
Copyright © 2003 Vertical Worship Songs/Sovereign Music UK

81
LEAD ME ON, LORD
lead me on.
Help me trust in your word.
Let it be as a lamp to my feet,
and a light for my path.
I have made my choice:
I'm following you.

Fill me up Lord, make me strong.
I'll depend on your word.
Let it be a safeguard for my mind,
and a shield for my soul.
I have set my heart on following you.

Lead me on, Lord, lead me on.
I will trust in you.
Fill me up, Lord, make me strong:
I will follow you.

81a The leading and direction of God
Psalm 119: 33–35

Teach me, O Lord, to follow your decrees;
then I will keep them to the end.
Give me understanding,
and I will keep your law
and obey it with all my heart.
Direct me in the path of your commands,
for there I find delight.

82
LET THE LIVING STONES CRY OUT

every son and daughter praise,
celebrate the wonders of his amazing grace.
See the temple of our God
now is with the hearts of men.
Hallelujah! Sing to him and his amazing grace.

Grace that gives to every sinner
more than we deserve.
As Jesus takes upon himself every sin and curse.

Praise to him who gave so freely such a sacrifice,
what undeserving riches flow
from the cross of Christ.

Let the living stones cry out...

Praise to him who by his Spirit
guides our willing hearts.
Each of us uniquely made and
gifted for our task.

See the story of redemption
written on each stone
in broken lives and shattered dreams
Jesus makes his home.

Let the living stones cry out...

82a Memorial of the Resurrection – Prima Luce

At dawn on the first day of the week
The women came to the tomb
The angel asked them, whom do you seek?
We seek Jesus of Nazareth who was crucified
Why seek the living among the dead?
If you have taken my Lord away,
tell me where you have laid him.
He is not here; he is risen as he promised:
We are witnesses of these things.

Risen Lord Jesus
as Mary Magdalene met you in the garden
on the morning of your resurrection,
so may we meet you today and every day.
Speak to us as you spoke to her:
reveal yourself as the living Lord,
renew our hope and kindle our joy,
and send us to share the good news with others;
for with the Father and the Holy Spirit
you live and reign, now and forever
Amen

Behold, I am with you always,
to the end of time.
And will come to reign among you in glory.
Alleluia!

Alleluia! Christ is risen.
He is risen indeed Alleluia!

83
LIGHT OF THE WORLD

you stepped down into darkness,
opened my eyes, let me see.
Beauty that made this heart adore you,
hope of a life spent with you.

So here I am to worship,
here I am to bow down,
here I am to say that you're my God:
you're altogether lovely, altogether worthy,
altogether wonderful to me.

King of all days, oh so highly exalted,
glorious in heaven above,
humbly you came to the earth you created,
all for love's sake became poor.

And I'll never know how much it cost
to see my sin upon that cross. (Repeat)

83a Made alive with Christ
Colossians 2: 13

When you were dead in your sins and in the uncircumcision of your sinful nature, God made you alive with Christ.

84
LIKE A MIGHTY RIVER
a pure and healing stream,
grace flows from the Saviour
to wash the guilty clean.
There's nothing we can offer,
no deed will ever earn,
the gift of his forgiveness
is free and undeserved.

*Dave Bilbrough. Copyright © 2004 Thankyou Music
adm. UK & Europe by Kingsway Music. Used by permission*

85
LONGING FOR LIGHT
we wait in darkness.
Longing for truth, we turn to you.
Make us your own, your holy people;
light for the world to see.

*Christ, be our light!
Shine in our hearts,
shine through the darkness.
Christ, be our light!
Shine in your church gathered today.*

Longing for peace, our world is troubled.
Longing for hope, many despair.
Your word alone has power to save us.
Make us your living voice.

Longing for food, many are hungry.
Longing for water, many still thirst.
Make us your bread, broken for others,
shared until all are fed.

Longing for shelter, many are homeless,
longing for warmth, many are cold.
Make us your building, sheltering others,
walls made of living stone.

Many the gifts, many the people,
many the hearts that yearn to belong.
Let us be servants to one another,
making your kingdom come.

*Bernadette Farrell
Copyright © OCP Publications*

85a A prayer of confession
Faithful and just God
who sent your Son into the world
not to condemn but to save it.
Help us to acknowledge our times of
presumption and self-righteousness,
challenge our thoughts and motives
when we begin to accuse others,
grant us your forgiveness and make us whole.
By the power of our Lord and Saviour
Jesus Christ who is alive and reigns with you
in the unity of the Holy Spirit,
one God, now and for ever.
Amen.

Copyright © 2004 Marie Birkinshaw

86
LOOKING FOR YOUR PRESENCE
it's time to seek your face;
may the windows of heaven open up today.
Let us flow with your rhythm,
the Spirit and the word,
and pick up your burdens,
walk the land and pray.

*Carrying you, carrying you,
into the city streets and homes.
Carrying you, carrying you,
we hear the footsteps of the Lord.*

Can your heavy glory, can your heavy glory,
can your heavy glory rest on me?

*Godfrey Birtill & Martin Scott
Copyright © 2002 Radical UK Music/Sovereign Music UK*

86a A telling place
Bless us Lord this day with vision.
May this place be a sacred place,
a telling place, where heaven and earth meet.

*Copyright © Northumbria Community Trust Ltd, Hetton Hall,
Chatton, Northumberland, NE66 5SD.*

87
LORD, HERE WE STAND
hand in hand,
praying together for every land.
Ready and willing to obey your call.
Caring and bringing your good news to all.
By loving others, we hope and pray
that all will see Jesus is living today, amen.
Lord here we stand, hand in hand.

*Ishmael & Irene Smale. Copyright © 2003 Thankyou Music
adm. UK & Europe by Kingsway Music. Used by permission*

87a You did that for me

You left your throne in heaven
to be born as a human baby
in squalor and poverty.
Jesus, you did that for me.

You lived here on this earth.
You knew what it was like
to taste disappointment and rejection.
Not even your friends stuck by you.
Jesus, you did that for me.

You were nailed to a cross,
in agony and shame,
despite having done nothing but love.
Jesus, you did that for me.

You died and rose to life again
defeating the enemy of our souls
once and for all.
Jesus, you did that for me.

You have gone to the darkest of places
and to the greatest of lengths
to rescue those you love.
Jesus, you did that for me.

Copyright © 2004 Mel Holden

88

LORD, I COME BEFORE YOUR THRONE OF GRACE

I find rest in your presence, and fulness of joy.
In worship and wonder I behold your face,
singing what a faithful God have I.

What a faithful God have I,
what a faithful God.
What a faithful God have I,
faithful in every way.

Lord of mercy, you have heard my cry;
through the storm you're the beacon,
my song in the night.
In the shelter of your wings,
hear my heart's reply,
singing what a faithful God have I.

Lord all sovereign, granting peace from heaven,
let me comfort those who suffer
with the comfort you have given.
I will tell of your great love
for as long as I live,
singing what a faithful God have I.

Robert & Dawn Critchley. Copyright © 1989 Thankyou Music
adm. UK & Europe by Kingsway Music. Used by permission

89

LORD, I COME

longing to know you.
Lord I come, drawn by your love.
Lord I come, longing to see your face
for you call me to come into the holiest place.

Lord I come because of Jesus,
Lord I come because he came;
Lord I bow as you reveal your face,
you have called me to come
into the holiest place.

What did I do to deserve your favour?
What did I do to deserve your grace?
Called by my name into your presence,
holy God.

Geraldine Latty. Copyright © 2000 Thankyou Music
adm. UK & Europe by Kingsway Music. Used by permission

89a The fulness of Christ
Ephesians 3:14–19

For this reason I kneel before the Father,
from whom his whole family in heaven
and on earth derives its name.

I pray that out of his glorious riches he may
strengthen you with power through his Spirit
in your inner being, so that Christ may dwell
in your hearts through faith.

And I pray that you, being rooted and
established in love, may have power, together
with all the saints, to grasp how wide
and long and high and deep is the love of
Christ, and to know this love that surpasses
knowledge – that you may be filled to the
measure of all the fulness of God.

90

LORD, I'M GRATEFUL

amazed at what you've done.
My finest efforts are filthy rags;
but I'm made righteous by trusting in the Son;
I have God's riches at Christ's expense!

'Cause it's grace; there's nothing I can do
to make you love me more,
to make you love me less than you do.
And by faith I'm standing on this stone
of Christ and Christ alone,
your righteousness is all that I need,
'cause it's grace.

continued over...

Called and chosen when I was far away,
you brought me into your family.
Free, forgiven, my guilt is washed away;
your loving kindness is life to me.

Grace loves the sinner,
loves all I am and all I'll ever be;
makes me a winner
whatever lies the devil throws at me.

Freely given but bought with priceless blood,
my life was ransomed at Calvary;
there my Jesus gave everything he could
that I might live for eternity.

91
LORD OF ALL CREATION
of water, earth and sky,
the heavens are your tabernacle;
glory to the Lord on high.

God of wonders beyond our galaxy,
you are holy, holy;
the universe declares your majesty.
You are holy, holy;
Lord of heaven and earth,
Lord of heaven and earth.

Early in the morning
I will celebrate the light,
as I stumble in the darkness
I will call your name by night.

Hallelujah! To the Lord of heaven and earth.
Hallelujah! To the Lord of heaven and earth.
Hallelujah! To the Lord of heaven and earth.

92
LORD, TURN YOUR FOOTSTEPS
towards these ruins
we need you here, we need you here.
Our homes are broken, our children are stolen;
we need you here, we need you here.

Our God and King, Ancient of Days,
Alpha, Omega, Jesus, Saviour;
work your deliverance in this place.
Yours is the night, yours is the day;
no-one is greater: come Lord, save us!
Work your deliverance in this place.

Lord, turn your footsteps towards these ruins;
we need you here, we need you here.
In these streets filled with darkness,
with our children fatherless;
we need you here, we need you here.

93
LORD, YOU ARE GOOD
and your mercy endureth forever.
Lord, you are good
and your mercy endureth forever.
(Repeat)

People from every nation and tongue,
from generation to generation.

We worship you, hallelujah, hallelujah.
We worship you, for who you are.
(Repeat)
And you are good.

93a To him who is able
Ephesians 3:20–21

Now to him who is able to do immeasurably
more than all we ask or imagine, according
to his power that is at work within us, to him
be glory in the church and in Christ Jesus
throughout all generations, for ever and ever!
Amen

94
MAY THE LOVE OF CHRIST
find a home in your heart,
may he dwell within you and never depart.
By faith be rooted in Christ's love,
completely filled with the fulness of God. (x3)

95
MERCY FLOWS
from your throne above
giving us hope so sure and infinite grace.

Peace that flows from your throne above
giving us hope so sure and infinite grace.

Merciful Lord, love is your name.

Take my life, have it all,
I'm living for you, mighty God.
Light my path, make it yours;
I'm following you my God.

Justice flows...

95a Come from heaven, living bread
From John 6: 51

Jesus, bread of life,
come from heaven and feed us,
that we may know eternal life.

Jesus, bread of life,
come from heaven and use us;
through us nourish your world.

Amen.

96

MY HEART IS FILLED WITH THANKFULNESS

to him who bore my pain;
who plumbed the depths of my disgrace
and gave me life again;
who crushed my curse of sinfulness,
and clothed me in his light,
and wrote his law of righteousness
with power upon my heart.

My heart is filled with thankfulness
to him who walks beside;
who floods my weaknesses with strength
and causes fear to fly;
whose every promise is enough
for every step I take;
sustaining me with arms of love
and crowning me with grace.

My heart is filled with thankfulness
to him who reigns above;
whose wisdom is my perfect peace,
whose every thought is love.
For every day I have on earth
is given by the King.
So I will give my life, my all,
to love and follow him.

97

MY LORD, YOU WORE NO ROYAL CROWN

you did not wield the powers of state,
nor did you need a scholar's gown
or priestly robe, to make you great.
You never used a killer's sword
to end an unjust tyranny;
your only weapon was your word,
for truth alone could set us free.

You did not live a world away,
in hermit's cell or desert cave,
but felt our pain, and shared each day
with those you came to seek and save.
You made no mean or cunning move,
chose no unworthy compromise,
but carved a track of burning love
through tangles of deceit and lies.

You came unequalled, undeserved,
to be what we were meant to be;
to serve, instead of being served –
a light for all the world to see.
So when I stumble, set me right;
command my life as you require;
let all your gifts be my delight
and you, my Lord, my one desire.

98

MY SOUL'S DESIRE IS TO SEE YOUR FACE

to dwell within your house of grace.
My soul's desire is to live your word,
and to learn the ways of God.

My soul's desire is for liberty,
to know Christ's risen life in me.
My soul's desire is in following
the example of my King.

For you alone can read my soul,
and all the longings that it holds.
And you alone can satisfy, O Lord, be my desire.

My soul's desire is to sing your praise,
to enter in through heaven's gates.
To gaze upon your holy light
and to serve you with all my might.

My soul's desire is to do your will
when trouble comes – to trust you still.
To know the wonder of your love,
love that I'm not worthy of.

99

NOTHING COULD TAKE YOUR LOVE AWAY

no treasure on this earth
could ever take your place.
You took my blame
and nailed it to a cross,
separated from my shame,
united with my God.

I could not leave this place
for your love is here.

You call me home again,
and draw me to my knees,
caught between your arms,
and rescued by your grace.
So let me hear the comfort of your voice,
for precious are your words,
and loving is your heart.

I could not leave this place
for your love is here.
Regarded as your child,
I am redeemed.

100

O FOR A THOUSAND TONGUES TO SING

my great redeemer's praise,
the glories of my God and King,
the triumphs of his grace!
Jesus, the name that charms our fears,
and bids our sorrows cease;
'tis music in the sinner's ears,
'tis life and health and peace.

O for a thousand tongues to sing
my great redeemer's praise,
to tell the world the glories of my God and King,
the triumphs of his grace!

He breaks the power of cancelled sin,
he sets the prisoner free;
his blood can make the foulest clean;
his blood availed for me.
He speaks, and listening to his voice,
new life the dead receive,
the mournful broken hearts rejoice,
the humble poor believe.

Hear him, you deaf, his praise, you dumb,
your loosened tongues employ.
You blind, behold your Saviour come,
and leap, you lame, for joy.

My gracious Master and my God,
assist me to proclaim,
and spread through all the earth abroad
the honours of your name.

He breaks the power of cancelled sin.
(He sets the prisoner free.)
His blood can make the foulest clean,
(His blood availed for me,)
and listening to his voice
(new life the dead receive,)
the broken hearts rejoice,
the humble poor receive.

100a A Creed
From Ephesians 3

Let us declare our faith in God.

We believe in God the Father,
from whom every family in heaven and on
earth is named.

We believe in God the Son,
who lives in our hearts through faith,
and fills us with his love.

We believe in God the Holy Spirit,
who strengthens us
with power from on high.

We believe in one God;
Father, Son and Holy Spirit.
Amen

101

O GOD OF GRACE

to whom belongs
the work that love eternal willed,
to right again our nature's wrongs,
to see our destinies fulfilled.
So still today your purpose proves
the end to which creation moves.

In every age your voice is heard,
the calling of your love divine,
by hearts responsive to your word
and sealed in covenant and sign.
Of old you led by cloud and flame:
we walk by faith in Jesus' name.

The way of Christ who came to save
is born of love, and life laid down;
to go with him to death and grave,
who set the cross before the crown.
And so his path of life to tread
who rose in glory from the dead.

For evermore his kingdom stands
when earth itself is past and gone;
our future hopes are in his hands
who calls his church to journey on:
to work his will, to watch, and pray
'Your kingdom come in this our day.'

Timothy Dudley-Smith
Copyright © Timothy Dudley-Smith in the countries of Europe
(including Great Britain and Ireland) and of Africa.

102
OPEN THE EYES OF MY HEART

Lord, open the eyes of my heart.
I want to see you,
I want to see you.
(Repeat)

To see you high and lifted up,
shining in the light of your glory.
Pour out your power and love,
as we sing holy, holy, holy.

Holy, holy, holy,
holy, holy, holy,
holy, holy, holy,
I want to see you.

Paul Baloche. Copyright © 1997
Integrity's Hosanna! Music/Sovereign Music UK

102a Prayer of humble access

We do not presume to come to this your
table, merciful Lord, trusting in our own
righteousness, but in your manifold and great
mercies.
We are not worthy so much as to
gather up the crumbs under your table.
But you are the same Lord whose nature is
always to have mercy.
Grant us therefore, gracious Lord, so to eat
the flesh of your dear Son Jesus Christ and to
drink his blood, that we may evermore dwell
in him and he in us.
Amen

From Common Worship: Services and Prayers for the Church of England.
Copyright © The Archbishops' Council 2000

103
OPENING OUR HEARTS TO YOU

focusing our eyes on you,
lifting up our hands to you,
singing out this song for you;
praises that will fill the skies,
raising you over our lives,
lifting up the Saviour high.

We give you the highest praise. (Repeat)

You are so amazing Lord,
a beautiful and mighty God,
compassionate and merciful,
glorious and powerful.
King over the universe,
wonderfully in love with us,
passionate about the earth.

James Gregory. Copyright © 2002 Thankyou Music
adm. UK & Europe by Kingsway Music. Used by permission

103a Come and see Jesus
From John 1:35–51 & 4:1–39

Come and see Jesus, the Lamb of God,
offering his life for all.
We believe in Jesus.

Come and see Jesus, the Messiah,
anointed by God and chosen.
We believe in Jesus.

Come and see Jesus,
foretold by Moses and the prophets.
We believe in Jesus.

Come and see Jesus, the Son of God
and King of Israel.
We believe in Jesus.

Come and see Jesus, the Son of Man,
whom angels long to serve.
We believe in Jesus.

Come and see Jesus, who knows each of us
through and through.
We believe in Jesus.

Come and see Jesus, the gift of God
and the water of life.
We believe in Jesus;
we will come to him.
We will follow Jesus;
we will worship him.

Copyright © Mark Earey

104
O THE DEEP, DEEP LOVE OF JESUS

vast, unmeasured, boundless, free.
Rolling as a mighty ocean,
in it's fullness over me.
Underneath me, all around me,
is the current of thy love.
Leading onward, leading homeward,
to my glorious rest above.
O the deep, deep love,
vast, unmeasured, boundless, free.
O the deep, deep love, in it's fullness over me.

O the deep, deep love of Jesus,
spread his praise from shore to shore.
How he loveth, ever loveth,
changeth never, never more.
How he watches o'er his loved ones,
died to call them all his own;
how for them he intercedeth,
watcheth o'er them from the throne.
O the deep, deep love,
spread his praise from shore to shore.
O the deep, deep love, changeth never, never more.

O the deep, deep love of Jesus,
love of every love the best.
Tis an ocean vast of blessing,
tis a haven sweet of rest.
O the deep, deep love of Jesus,
tis a heav'n of heavens to me.
And it lifts me up to glory,
for it lifts me up to thee.
O the deep, deep love,
love of every love the best.
O the deep, deep love, tis a haven sweet of rest.

S.T. Francis (1834-1925)

105
OUR GOD IS A GREAT BIG GOD

our God is a great big God,
our God is a great big God
and he holds us in his hands.

He's higher than a skyscraper,
and he's deeper than a submarine.
He's wider than the universe
and beyond my wildest dreams.

He's known me and he's loved me
since before the world began.
How wonderful to be a part of
God's amazing plan.

Nigel & Jo Hemming. Copyright © 2001 Vineyard Songs (UK/Eire)
adm. CopyCare. Used by permission.

106
PRAISE THE LORD FROM THE HEAVENS

praise him from the skies.
Praise the Lord, hosts of angels,
sing celestial choirs.
Praise him sun and moon,
praise him shining stars,
clouds that ride on the wind;
let everything with life and breath
praises sing.

Praise the Lord, earth and oceans,
creatures of the deep.
Fire and hail, ice and hurricane,
let the thunder speak.
Beasts of forest, field and desert,
every bird in the sky;
from least of all to greatest king
sing for joy.

Let them all praise the one name
worthy of all praise.
Only God, our Creator
from eternal days.
All his excellence far outshining,
all the worlds he has made;
yet comes to us, delivers us
give him praise.

To the Lord of all creation,
glory and majesty forever.
To the Lord of all creation,
glory and majesty forever.
Praise the Lord of all creation,
glory and majesty forever.

All his excellence far outshining,
all the worlds he has made;
yet comes to us, delivers us,
give him praise.

Graham Kendrick/Psalm 148
Copyright © 2004 Make Way Music. International copyright secured
All rights reserved. Used by permission.

107
PRAISE THE LORD
praise the Lord,
all you servants of our God,
who stand by night in the holy place,
to come and seek his face.
(Repeat)

Praise the Lord, praise the Lord,
for his kindness never fails,
for he is good, his love endures,
both now and evermore.

For no-one else is worthy,
you alone are holy.
I'll bring you all honour and praise.
Lord, you are strong and mighty,
the earth displays your glory,
so I give you all my praise,
Lord, I give you all my praise.

108
REBUILD YOUR TEMPLE
O merciful God,
restore this nation, please.
Rekindle embers once burning with heat,
return us to our knees.
Revive this body, O kiss of life,
renew our vision, please.
Create new wineskins to carry new blood;
would you your truth release?

Let your kingdom come,
your will be done,
on earth as it is in heaven.
Let your kingdom come,
your will be done,
on earth as it is in heaven.

Reverse this current that's flowing away,
rebuke our pride, Lord, please.
Remove religion that hides from your face,
would you this moment seize?
Reveal the blueprints
to where you would lead,
release dry wood to die.
Redeem your children as promised of old,
for them, to you, we cry.

109
SAVIOUR, LORD, YOU KNOW MY HEART
let me be surrendered to your will.
Though it costs everything,
I give it all to bring
a life that is devoted to your way.

Jesus thank you for your love,
the love that gives me shelter from the storm.
Held in your wounded hands,
forever I will stand,
safe beneath the shadow of your cross.

For blessed are the ones who seek you,
blessed are the ones who trust you,
blessed are the ones who fear your name.

Hallelujah! Hallelujah!
What a Saviour, hallelujah!

110
SEE, WHAT A MORNING
gloriously bright,
with the dawning of hope in Jerusalem;
folded the grave-clothes,
tomb filled with light,
as the angels announce Christ is risen!
See God's salvation plan, wrought in love,
borne in pain, paid in sacrifice,
fulfilled in Christ, the man,
for he lives: Christ is risen from the dead!

See Mary weeping, 'Where is he laid?'
As in sorrow she turns from the empty tomb;
hears a voice speaking, calling her name;
it's the Master, the Lord raised to life again!
The voice that spans the years,
speaking life, stirring hope, bringing peace to us,
will sound till he appears,
for he lives, Christ is risen from the dead!

One with the Father, Ancient of Days,
through the Spirit who clothes faith with certainty,
honour and blessing, glory and praise
to the King crowned with power and authority!
And we are raised with him,
death is dead, love has won, Christ has conquered;
and we shall reign with him,
for he lives, Christ is risen from the dead!

111

SING TO THE LORD

for he is good,
give thanks to him.
Tell all the world of all he's done.
Come lift your voice to worship him,
come shout aloud.
Open up you gates, you ancient doors;
let his glory in.

Hallelujah, King forever,
all the earth will bow.
God most holy, you're so worthy,
we will praise you now.

He is a God of favour, mercy and grace;
he reaches out with arms held wide.
Who is this King of glory?
He's Lord of all.
Open up you gates, you ancient doors,
let his glory in.

Let the heavens rejoice, let the earth be glad.
Let the seas resound with praise.
Let us join as one, with creation's song
lifting up a sound of praise.

112

SOVEREIGN LORD OVER ALL

you are reigning forever.
Worship flows from our lips,
we have come for just one glimpse.

And we sing hallelujah, hallelujah, hallelujah.

Majesty, reign in me,
your right hand enfolding me.
Earth applaud, heavens sing at the sight
of Christ the King.

Lord of lords, now enthroned,
who can stand in your presence?
Fire of love, holy One,
you burn brighter than the sun.

113

TAKE MY LIFE AND LET IT BE

all you purpose, Lord, for me.
Consecrate my passing days,
let them flow in ceaseless praise.

Take my hands and let them move
at the impulse of your love.

Take my feet and let them run
with the news of victory won.

Giving it all to you,
I'm losing my life to you,
I'm choosing to follow you today.
I'm giving it all to you,
I'm losing my life to you:
Jesus, have it all your way.

Take my voice and let me sing
always, only for my King.
Take my lips, let them proclaim
all the beauty of your name.

Take my wealth, all I possess,
make me rich in faithfulness.
Take my mind that I may use
every power as you shall choose.

Take my love, my Lord, I pour
at your feet its treasure store.
Take myself and I will be,
yours for all eternity.

I'm giving it all to you...

113a Jesus – the living bread

Living Father God
who sent your Son to the world to be the
bread of heaven
and to raise us to life on the last day,
feed and revitalise us with this bread;
nourish us with all goodness
and sustain us that we might always serve you.
By the grace of our Lord and Saviour Jesus
Christ who is alive and reigns with you
in the unity of the Holy Spirit,
one God, now and for ever.
Amen.

114a Belonging
1 Peter 2: 9–10

You are a chosen people, a royal priesthood, a
holy nation, a people belonging to God, that
you may declare the praises of him who called
you out of darkness into his wonderful light.
Once you were not a people, but now you are
the people of God; once you had not received
mercy, but now you have received mercy.

114

THANK YOU FOR THE CROSS, LORD

Thank you for the price you paid.
Bearing all my sin and shame,
in love you came and gave amazing grace.

Thank you for this love, Lord.
Thank you for the nail pierced hands.
Washed me in your cleansing flow,
now all I know; your forgiveness and embrace.

Worthy is the Lamb, seated on the throne.
Crown you now with many crowns,
you reign victorious.
High and lifted up, Jesus, Son of God;
the Darling of heaven, crucified.
Worthy is the Lamb, worthy is the Lamb.

115

TENDER SAVIOUR

hold me fast,
soothe this troubled soul at last;
and heal the wounds of all that's past,
tender Saviour.

Tender Saviour, speak to me,
whisper words of hope and peace,
and let the tumult in me cease,
tender Saviour.

And I will not give up this quest
'til I know I am blest,
for I come in my brokenness,
tender Saviour.

Tender Saviour, hear my cry,
look with pity on this child;
and show your mercy by and by,
tender Saviour.

And I will not give up...

Tender Saviour, make it so,
let your blessings overflow.
Until you do, I won't let go;
tender Saviour.

And I will not give up this quest
'til I know I am blest,
forever in your arms at rest,
tender Saviour.

115a Circle us

Circle me /us / them / … Lord
keep protection near and danger afar
Circle me / us / them / … Lord
keep hope within, keep despair without
Circle me / us / them / … Lord
keep light near, and darkness afar
Circle me / us / them / … Lord
keep peace within and anxiety out.
The eternal Father, Son and Holy Spirit
shield me / us / them / … on every side.
Amen.

116

THE LORD IS GRACIOUS AND COMPASSIONATE

slow to anger and rich in love.
The Lord is gracious and compassionate
slow to anger and rich in love.

The Lord is good to all,
he has compassion on all that he has made.

As far as the east is from the west,
that's how far he has removed
our transgressions from us.
As far as the east is from the west,
that's how far he has removed
our transgressions from us.

Praise the Lord, oh my soul.
praise the Lord.
(Repeat)

117

THE LOVE OF GOD COMES CLOSE

where stands an open door
to let the stranger in,
to mingle rich and poor.
The love of God is here to stay,
embracing those who walk his way.

The peace of God comes close
to those caught in the storm,
foregoing lives of ease
to ease the lives forlorn.
The peace of God is here to stay,
embracing those who walk his way.

continued over...

The joy of God comes close
where faith encounters fears,
where heights and depths of life
are found through smiles and tears.
The joy of God is here to stay,
embracing those who walk his way.

The grace of God comes close
to those whose grace is spent,
when hearts are tired or sore
and hope is bruised or bent.
The grace of God is here to stay,
embracing those who walk his way.

The Son of God comes close
where people praise his name,
where bread and wine are blest
and shared as when he came.
The Son of God is here to stay,
embracing those who walk his way.

117a God about me

God before me
God behind me
God above me
God beneath me
God's love about me
God's strength surround me
God all about me
God deep within me
God's grace toward me.

118

THERE ARE SHADOWS
CAST ACROSS THE SUN

from the darkness of our hearts,
from the barricades and prejudice
that can tear this world apart.
And so, Lord, we come to find in you
a clear and guiding light,
that can shine beyond our differences
with a Spirit that unites.

To the one God, over all things,
in earth and heaven above.
To the one God, let our praises sing:
one God, King of love.

You are Father God to everyone,
from the greatest to the least;
to the powerful and the powerless,
in the west and in the east.

And now, Lord, we long to bring to you
our undivided hearts;
to be melted by the fire of love,
into you to be a part.

Through the nails that held you to the cross,
that were forged within love's flame:
to the promise of eternal life
that is signed in Jesus' name.
By the grace of one who died for all,
and rose to life again;
you have shown your love for all the world
has no limits and no end.

119

THERE IS A HIGHER THRONE

than all this world has known,
where faithful ones from every tongue
will one day come.
Before the Son we'll stand,
made faultless through the Lamb;
believing hearts find promised grace,
salvation comes.

Hear heaven's voices sing,
their thunderous anthem rings;
through emerald courts and sapphire skies
their praises rise.
All glory, wisdom, power,
strength, thanks and honour are
to God, our King, who reigns on high
forever more.

And there we'll find our home,
our life before the throne;
we'll honour him in perfect song,
where we belong.
He'll wipe each tear-stained eye,
as thirst and hunger die;
the Lamb becomes our Shepherd King,
we'll reign with him.

120

THERE IS A HOPE SO SURE

a promise so secure:
the mystery of God at last made known.
Treasures so vast appear,
all wisdom, knowledge here:
it's Christ in us, the hope of glory!

And the life that I now live, no longer is my own,
Jesus lives in me the hope of glory.
And each day I live, no longer is my own,
Jesus lives in me the hope of glory.

There is a life so true,
a life of love so pure,
for all our sin a perfect sacrifice.
And when that life was nailed,
on cruel cross impaled,
our sinful flesh with him was crucified.

There is a life so strong,
that a whole world of wrong,
and all the powers of hell could not defeat.
For Jesus rose again,
and if we died with him,
with him we'll rise to share his endless life.

120a   You are my fortress

Living under the protection of God Most High,
staying under the shadow of God all powerful.
We will declare to the Lord:

You are my fortress, my place of safety;
you are my God, I trust you,
my hope is in you.

121
THERE IS A RIVER
flowing free;
it's the love of Jesus,
let it wash over me.
It's as vast as the ocean,
it's as wide as the sea,
it's the love of Jesus,
let it wash over me.

Exactly as I am,
I come without one plea;
in absolute surrender,
to you I'll bow my knee.

My glory is the cross,
the blood you shed for me,
in absolute surrender,
to you I'll bow my knee.

122
THERE MUST BE MORE THAN THIS
O breath of God, come breathe within.
There must be more than this:
Spirit of God, we wait for you.
Fill us anew, we pray; fill us anew, we pray.

Consuming Fire, fan into flame
a passion for your name.
Spirit of God, fall in this place.
Lord, have your way,
Lord, have your way with us.

Come like a rushing wind,
clothe us in power from on high.
Now set the captives free;
leave us abandoned to your praise.
Lord, let your glory fall. (x2)

122a Lord of all Grace

Lord of all grace, help us as recovering sinners
to drink of the wellspring of your love
and know the blessing of your healing,
restoring our lives with the beauty
and freedom of holiness.

123
THERE'S A LOT OF PAIN
but a lot more healing,
there's a lot of trouble, but a lot more peace.
There's a lot of hate, but a lot more loving,
there's a lot of sin, but a lot more grace.

Oh, outrageous grace! (x2)
Love unfurled by heavens hand.
Oh, outrageous grace! (x2)
Through my Jesus I can stand.

There's a lot of fear, but a lot more freedom;
there's a lot of darkness, but a lot more light.
There's a lot of cloud, but a lot more vision;
there's a lot of perishing, but a lot more life.

There's an enemy,
that seeks to kill what it can't control.
It twists and turns,
making mountains out of molehills.
But I will call on the Lord who is worthy of praise;
I run to him... and I am saved!

124

THIS IS THE ANTHEM OF THE FREE

this is the song of the redeemed,
Jesus, your praises rising higher
and higher and higher.
We'll sing it loud, we'll sing it strong,
we'll sing it all around the world,
Jesus, your praise will last forever and ever and ever.

Hear the sound of the free,
hear the cry of liberty,
we will rejoice in you, we will rejoice.
As we sing of all you've done,
and the wonders of your love,
we will rejoice in you, we will rejoice.

Rising up around the earth
is a heavenly song
of your endless worth,
growing louder and louder and louder.

This is the anthem of the free...

Then one day your heavenly song
will drown all music but its own.
(Repeat)

124a   Christ with us

Christ behind us in all of our yesterdays.
Christ with us in our today.
Christ before us in all of our tomorrows,
Alpha and omega, Christ, Lord of all!

125

THROUGH DAYS OF RAGE AND WONDER

we pursue the end of time,
to seize the day eternal,
the reign of love divine.
Our ancient rites of passage
still are the bread and wine:
our hope, a cross that towers
over the wrecks of time.

Through days of rage and wonder,
by the awesome power of prayer
God will shake every nation,
secrets will be laid bare.

And if his light increasing
casts deeper shadows here,
safe in his holy presence,
love will cast out our fear.

Through days of rage and wonder,
you will give us grace to stand
and seek a heavenly city
not built by human hands.
Now is the only moment
within our power to change:
to give back in obedience
while life and breath remain.

Fixing our eyes on Jesus,
we will press on day by day;
this world's vain passing pleasures
are not our destiny.
Our ancient rites of passage
still are the bread and wine:
our hope a cross that towers
over the wrecks of time.

And our eyes are on you,
our eyes are on you.
Lord, our eyes are on you,
our eyes are on you.

125a Showered with love
Based on Ephesians 1: 1–14

I was unwanted and you chose me;
unloved and you loved me.

I was drifting through life, uncertain
and you gave a purpose to my life.

Once rootless, I now belong to you.
Once alienated, I have been redeemed
and reconciled to God.

When I was guilty, you forgave all my sins,
when bankrupt you gave me the riches
of your grace.

When puzzled, you showed me all wisdom
and understanding.
When excluded, I heard you whisper
the mystery of your will.

Once there was no point to my life
but you have marked me with your Spirit
and made me for the praise of your glory.

Allelujah!

126

THOUGH I'VE SEEN TROUBLES

you will restore my life again.
Though I've been wounded, and tasted bitterness
from the depths of the earth
you always bring me up again,
increase my honour and comfort me.

Thank you for your faithfulness, O my God.
I love you, and my lips will shout for joy,
and my song declare your glory
all day long, all day long.

Through disappointments you breathe
encouragement and hope.
My lack of wisdom you've often overlooked.
Blown away by your grace
and by the power in the blood
I grow in freedom, rooted in love.

126a A shout of Joy
From Luke 24: 6

He is not here
He is risen
Allelujah!

127

TO GOD OUR GREAT SALVATION

a triumph-song we raise,
with hymns of adoration
and everlasting praise.
That name beyond all naming,
from age to age adored,
we lift on high proclaiming
the greatness of the Lord.

Declare in song and story
the wonders we confess,
who hail the King of glory –
the Lord, our righteousness.
In loving-kindness caring,
his mercies stand displayed:
forgiving and forbearing,
to all his hand has made.

His kingdom knows no ending,
enthroned in life sublime.
His sovereign power extending
beyond all space and time.
To us and all things living
he comes in word and deed,
forbearing and forgiving,
to meet us in our need.

The King of all creation
is near to those who call;
the God of our salvation
has stooped to save us all.
Lift high your hearts and voices,
his praises sound again.
In God his earth rejoices
for evermore. Amen!

128

WE ARE A SHINING LIGHT

city on a hill that can't be hidden;
a shining light.
And this shining light is the life of Jesus in us;
oh what a light.

The fire of his Spirit burns
with justice, joy and peace
and works through our hands and feet.

Go do something beautiful
in the name of Jesus
do something beautiful.
Go do something Jesus would;
do something beautiful, do something beautiful.

We are the salt of the earth
here to purify and flavour; salt of the earth.
Sent through all the earth
to love God and love our neighbour;
salt of the earth.

As freely as we received, so freely we must give
and we are his hands and feet.

Chorus

Let your light so shine before the world,
that all may see the good you do,
and give their praise to God our Father.

129

WE COME IN YOUR NAME

for all things you have made,
and by your word all things you sustain.
The Lamb that was slain for our sins lives to reign;
the Lord of all, name above all names!

We have been saved by faith into your glorious name,
and this a gift of grace, freely given us.
Now all our sins are gone, defeated at the cross
and we now live in you,
raised with you by the power of God!

continued over...

You have been lifted to the highest place
and you now live and rule forever!
We come to bring to you the highest praise,
for you are King of kings forever:
Son of God, Jesus!

Holy is the Lamb, worthy of glory,
worthy of honour.
High and lifted up,
and seated in majesty,
your throne will last forever.
(Repeat)

... forevermore.

130
WE ARE BOWED BEFORE YOU
our hearts are open wide,
Lord, would you visit us again?
We are desperate people,
who long to feel your hand,
would you come in power and break in?

Fill this house, fill this place,
fill this temple of praise;
show us your glory.
Fill this house, fill this place,
fill this temple of praise;
show us your glory, show us your glory.

May our eyes be opened
to your everlasting hope,
may your Spirit captivate our lives.
Deeper revelation,
a closer walk with you;
filled with passion we will rise.

130a   True humility

When the Lord Jesus washed his disciples' feet,
he demonstrated our equality in God's
community of grace.
In our worship now may we discover afresh
the true humility that comes from Christ
and be empowered to love and serve one
another in the way he commands us.
In Jesus name, Amen.

131
WHAT WONDER OF GRACE IS THIS
what story of passion divine;
where judgement and mercy kiss,
where power and love are entwined?
No tongue can speak this glory,
no words express the joy you bring
as I enter the courts of the King.

My desire is to come to this place,
my desire is to look on your face,
perfect in beauty, in truth and love,
your glory shines over all the earth;
the King who lavishes grace on us is here.

Your will is my daily bread,
enough for my plenty and need;
I'll live by the words you've said,
and follow wherever you lead.
And though my flesh may fail me,
you prove your grace in all I do;
Lord my heart is devoted to you.

131a God's transforming power

May the Lord bless you and transform you
by his grace, mercy and love.

132
WHEN I WAS LOST
you came and rescued me;
reached down in to the pit and lifted me.
O Lord, such love,
I was as far from you as I could be.
You know all the things I've ever done,
but Jesus' blood has cancelled every one.
O Lord, such grace
to qualify me as your own.

There is a new song in my mouth,
there is a deep cry in my heart,
a hymn of praise to Almighty God – hallelujah!
And now I stand firm on this Rock,
my life is hidden now with Christ in God.
The old has gone and the new has come –
hallelujah!
Your love has lifted me.

Now I have come into your family,
for the Son of God has died for me.
O Lord, such peace.
I am as loved by you as I could be.

In the full assurance of your love
now with every confidence we come.
O Lord, such joy
to know that you delight in me.

Many are the wonders you have done,
and many are the things that you have planned.
How beautiful the grace that gives to us
all that we don't deserve,
all that we cannot earn, but is a gift of love –
your love has lifted me.

133
WHO IS MOVING ON THE WATERS
who is holding up the moon,
who is peeling back the darkness
with the burning light of noon?
Who is standing on the mountains,
who is on the earth below,
who is bigger than the heavens,
and the lover of my soul?

*Creator God; he is Yahweh.
The great 'I Am'; he is Yahweh.
The Lord of all; he is Yahweh.
Rose of Sharon; he is Yahweh.
The righteous Son; he is Yahweh;
the Three-in-One; he is Yahweh.*

Who is he that makes me happy,
who is he that gives me peace,
who is he that brings me comfort,
and turns the bitter into sweet?
Who is he that turns my passion,
who is rising up in me,
who is filling up my hunger
with everything I need?

You are holy and eternal,
and forever you will reign.
Every knee will bow before you,
every tongue will confess your name.
All the angels give you glory,
as they stand before your throne.
And here on earth we gather
to declare your name alone.

134
WONDERFUL GRACE
that gives what I don't deserve,
pays me what Christ has earned,
then lets me go free.

Wonderful grace,
that gives me the time to change,
washes away the stains that once covered me.

*And all that I have I lay at the feet
of the wonderful Saviour who loves me.*

Wonderful love, that held in the face of death,
breathed in its latest breath
forgiveness for me.
Wonderful love,
whose power can break every chain,
giving us life again, setting us free.

135
WONDERFUL, SO WONDERFUL
is your unfailing love,
your cross has spoken mercy over me.
No eye has seen, no ear has heard,
no heart could fully know
how glorious, how beautiful you are.

*Beautiful one I love,
beautiful one I adore,
beautiful one my soul must sing.*

Powerful, so powerful,
your glory fills the skies,
your mighty works are displayed for all to see.
The beauty of your majesty
awakes my heart to sing:
how marvellous, how wonderful you are.

You opened my eyes to your wonders anew,
you captured my heart with this love,
'cos nothing on earth is as beautiful as you.

135a All that I do

All that I am Lord, I place into your hands Lord
All that I do Lord, I place into your hands Lord
Everything I work for, I place into your hands Lord
Those whom I work with,
I place into your hands Lord
Everything I hope for, I place into your hands Lord
The troubles that weary me,
I place into your hands Lord
The thoughts that disturb me,
I place into your hands Lord
Each one I pray for, I place into your hands Lord
Each that I care for, I place into your hands Lord

136
YOU ARE GOD IN HEAVEN
and here am I on earth;
so I'll let my words be few:
Jesus, I am so in love with you.

And I'll stand in awe of you,
yes, I'll stand in awe of you.
And I'll let my words be few:
Jesus, I am so in love with you.

The simplest of all love songs
I want to bring to you;
so I'll let my words be few:
Jesus, I am so in love with you.

136a Keep us silent before you
Prayer based on Revelation 8: 1

Your purpose, Lord God, silences heaven.
Forgive our empty chatter,
our mindless gossip in your presence.
Keep us silent before you.

Your purpose, Lord God, silences heaven.
How awesome is your justice,
how great your victory!
Keep us silent before you.

Your purpose, Lord God, silences heaven.
Angels and archangels await your bidding,
cherubim and seraphim stand on your
summons.
Keep us silent before you.

Paul Sheppy

137
YOU ARE RIGHTEOUS
you love justice,
and those who honour you will see your face.

I will arise and lift my eyes
to see your majesty, your holiness.
And all I am will bless you.

My hope is in the name of the Lord,
where my help comes from.
You're my strength, my song.
My trust is in the name of the Lord.
I will sing your praise, you are faithful.

138
YOU ARE THE LORD
the famous one, famous one;
great is your name in all the earth.
The heavens declare you're glorious, glorious;
great is your fame beyond the earth.

And for all you've done and yet to do,
with every breath, I'm praising you.
Desire of nations and every heart,
you alone are God, you alone are God.

The Morning Star is shining through,
and every eye is watching you.
Revealed by nature and miracles
you are beautiful, you are beautiful.

138a   We have come

Living God, Father, Son and Holy Spirit,
sacred Trinity.
We have come alone from many places
to be together.

Living God who caused Spring Harvest into
being.
We have come to acknowledge your
presence and to seek your face.

Living God, creator of the world,
redeemer of humanity, God with us.
We have journeyed alone to a place
where our journeys meet.

Living God, sustainer and inspirer,
protector and restorer, the one in whom we
live and move and have our being.
We have come to worship, to share, to
learn, and to be renewed.
Have mercy on us. Amen.

139
YOU CAME FROM HEAVEN
to live on the earth;
your glory you laid aside.
You humbled yourself and you lived just to serve,
fulfilling God's purpose and plan.

You're the King of kings, above all things,
in heaven and on the earth.
You reign in majesty, rule in sovereignty,
the holy King of all.

You were obedient to death on the cross,
in dying you took my place.
Now raised up in glory and at the right hand,
your name is above every name.

Every knee must bow and every tongue confess:
Jesus Christ is Lord.
(Repeat)

140
YOU CHOSE THE CROSS
with every breath,
the perfect life, the perfect death:
you chose the cross.
A crown of thorns you wore for us,
and crowned us with eternal life:
you chose the cross.
And though your soul was overwhelmed with pain,
obedient to death you overcame.

I'm lost in wonder, I'm lost in love,
I'm lost in praise forever more.
Because of Jesus' unfailing love,
I am forgiven, I am restored.

You loosed the cords of sinfulness
and broke the chains of my disgrace:
you chose the cross.
Up from the grave victorious
you rose again so glorious:
you chose the cross.
The sorrow that surrounded you was mine,
'yet not my will but yours be done' you said.

140a A blessing of Grace
Ephesians 6: 24

Grace to all who love our Lord Jesus Christ
with an undying love.

141
YOU COLOUR THIS WORLD BEAUTIFUL
sparkle like the brightest jewel.
All the stars across the sky
couldn't match you if they tried
for your beauty is beyond imagination.

Creation hangs on every word,
spoken by the Son of God,
and you perfectly reflect
all the glory of our God,
for your power is beyond our comprehension.

This is you, Jesus; this is you.
This is you, Jesus; this is you.

Teacher, healer, holy One,
image of the living God;
this is you.
Came to earth to save the lost,
live and die like one of us,
this is you.

This is you, this is you.

142
YOU FORMED US FROM THE DUST
you breathed your breath in us,
we are the work of your hands.
Now we breathe back to you
love songs of gratitude,
adoring you with all we have.

We were created
to worship your name,
and we were created
to bring you our praise.

If we don't worship you,
we'll search for substitutes
to fill the void in our hearts.
Worshipping other things
destroys our liberty,
but as we praise you, we are free.

We were created
to worship your name,
and we were created
to bring you our praise.

So we will worship,
so we will praise you,
our Creator for all our days.

For this is what we were made to do.
For this is what we were made to do.
For this is what we were made to do.
So we lift up our praise to you.

142a Always giving thanks
From Ephesians 5: 19–20

We will rejoice in you with all our hearts,
our lives will sing your praise.
Alleluia!

143

YOU POUR OUT GRACE

on the broken-hearted,
and you lift the hope of the weary soul,
and you stretch out your hand
with your loving mercy.
You saw this heart that was lost and broken,
and you felt the pain of my loneliness,
and you befriended me
and restored my dignity.

You alone revealed the love of God to me,
and you alone have given everything for me;
and you alone deserve the highest praise, Jesus.

You demonstrated the life of love to me,
and how it was that you wanted me to live.
Heart of compassion and hands of healing:
I need your Spirit to help accomplish this.
Abundant grace and your strength in weakness,
the steady hand of the Father holding me.

You alone revealed...

And you have given me great salvation,
and you have given me hope eternal,
and every day I will look to give you
all the glory that's due your name.

Gareth Robinson & Joannah Oyeniran
Copyright © 2001 Thankyou Music
adm. UK & Europe by Kingsway Music. Used by permission

143a   A prayer of service

Ever-living God, we give thanks that all
authority in heaven and on earth belongs
to your Son Jesus who, in a world where
humility is often seen as a sign of weakness,
still chose to wash his disciples' feet.
Help us to see how Christ's actions can
bring revolution to the realm of human
relationships and teach us how best to offer
our lives in service as messengers of your
truth by the grace of our Master and Lord,
Jesus Christ, who is alive and reigns with you
in the unity of the Holy Spirit,
one God, now and for ever.
Amen.

Copyright © 2004 Marie Birkinshaw

144

YOU SPREAD OUT THE SKIES

over empty space;
said 'Let there be light'
to a dark and formless world,
your light was born.

You spread out your arms
over empty hearts;
said 'Let there be light',
to a dark and hopeless world
your Son was born.

You made the world
and saw that it was good.
You sent your only Son,
for you are good.

What a wonderful Maker,
what a wonderful Saviour;
how majestic your whispers
and how humble your love.
With a strength like no other
and the heart of a Father;
how majestic your whispers,
what a wonderful God.

No eye has fully seen
how beautiful the cross
and we have only heard the faintest whispers
of how great you are.

Matt Redman & Chris Tomlin. Copyright © 2002 worshiptogether.com
songs/Six Steps Music/Adm. by Kingsway Music.
For the UK & Europe. Used by permission.

144a The Mercy of God
Lamentations 3:22–23

Because of the Lord's great love we are not
consumed,
for his compassions never fail.
They are new every morning;
great is your faithfulness.

145

YOU'RE KING AND YOU
REIGN OVER ALL THINGS

You're King – and you reign over all.
You're King – and you reign over all things.
You're King – and you reign over all.

Jesus – the glory goes to you.
Jesus – to you all praise is due.
Jesus – we choose to worship you.
You're King and you reign over all.

Over the invisible, over the visible;
over all powers and kingdoms.
(x3)
You're King and you reign over all.

Geraldine Latty & Carey Luce. Copyright © 2003 Thankyou Music
adm. UK & Europe by Kingsway Music. Used by permission

146

YOU'RE THE WORD OF GOD THE FATHER

from before the world began.
Every star and every planet
has been fashioned by your hand.
All creation holds together
by the power of your voice;
let the skies declare your glory,
let the land and seas rejoice.

You're the author of creation,
you're the Lord of every man
and your cry of love rings out across the lands.

Yet you left the gaze of angels,
came to seek and save the lost
and exchanged the joy of heaven
for the anguish of a cross.
With a prayer you fed the hungry,
with a word you stilled the sea;
yet how silently you suffered
that the guilty may go free.

With a shout you rose victorious,
wresting victory from the grave
and ascended into heaven
leading captives in your wake.
Now you stand before the Father
interceding for your own,
from each tribe and tongue and nation
you are leading sinners home.

Keith Getty & Stuart Townend. Copyright © 2002 Thankyou Music
adm. UK & Europe by Kingsway Music. Used by permission

146a Collect of Easter Sunday

Lord of all life and power,
who through the mighty resurrection of your
Son overcame the old order of sin and death
to make all things new in him;
grant that we, being dead to sin
and alive to you in Jesus Christ,
may reign with him in glory;

To whom with you and the Holy Spirit
be praise and honour, glory and might,
now and in all eternity. **Amen**

Material from Celebrating Common Prayer (Mowbray)
© The Society of Saint Francis 1992, is used with permission.

147

YOUR LOVE IS AMAZING

steady and unchanging;
your love is a mountain, firm beneath my feet.
Your love is a mystery, how you gently lift me;
when I am surrounded, your love carries me.

Hallelujah, hallelujah,
hallelujah, your love makes me sing.
Hallelujah, hallelujah,
hallelujah, your love makes me sing.

Your love is surprising, I can feel it rising,
all the joy that's growing deep inside of me.
Every time I see you,
all your goodness shines through
and I can feel this God song,
rising up in me.

Brenton Brown & Brian Doerksen. Copyright © 2000
Vineyard Songs (UK/Eire) adm. CopyCare. Used by permission.

147a Irish blessing

May the road rise to meet you;
may the wind be always at your back.
May the sun shine warm upon your face,
and the rain fall soft upon your fields,
until we meet again.
May God hold you
in the hollow of His hand.

Copyright © Northumbria Community Trust Ltd, Hetton Hall,
Chatton, Northumberland, NE66 5SD.

148

YOUR LOVE IS EVERLASTING

it's an everlasting love;
your mercy is as new
as every rising of the sun,
and your loving kindness,
loving kindness, is better than life.

Your grace is all-sufficient,
it's an all-sufficient grace;
your power and your glory
are forever on display,
and your loving kindness,
your loving kindness, is better than life.

Oh, it's better,
oh, better than life;
oh, so much better;
Jesus your loving kindness
is better than life.

Fairest of ten thousand,
of ten thousand you are fair,
and nothing in this world
could ever measure or compare
to your loving kindness,
your loving kindness
is better than life.

continued over...

All your ways are just, oh Lord,
you're just in all your ways,
and I will lift my hands, oh Lord,
with gratitude and praise,
for your loving kindness,
your loving kindness,
is better than life.

Jesus, your loving kindness
is better than life itself,
better than life itself.
Jesus your loving kindness
is better than life itself
better than life.

148a Compassionate and gracious God
From Exodus 34: 6

Lord of all might, majesty, power and comfort
You are the compassionate and gracious God

149
YOUR LOVE

shining like the sun,
pouring like the rain,
raging like the storm,
refreshing me again.
Ooh, I receive your love.

Your grace frees me from the past,
it purges every sin,
it purifies my heart
and heals me from within.
Ooh, I receive your grace.

Pour over me, pour over me,
let your rain flood this thirsty soul.
Pour over me your waves of love,
pour over me.

I come and lay my burden down
gladly at your feet,
I'm opening up my heart,
come make this joy complete.
Ooh, I receive your peace.

150
YOUR LOVING KINDNESS

is better than life,
so will I bless thee while I live.
I'll lift my hands up in your holy name;
your loving kindness is better than life.

My soul is satisfied with the fullness of your love,
my mouth shall sing your praise forever more.
With joy and gladness I'll sing your glory,
for you are great and greatly to be praised!

The abundance of your grace I've seen in my life,
your peace and mercy surround me everyday.
With joy and gladness I'll sing your glory,
for you are great and greatly to be praised!

Early in the morning will I praise your name,
I'll glory in you in the afternoon.
And in the evening I will meditate,
for you are great and greatly to be praised!

150a A Trinitarian blessing
2 Corinthians 13: 14

May the grace of the Lord Jesus Christ,
and the love of God, and the fellowship of
the Holy Spirit be with you all.

Spoken worship Index

2a	Collect for Palm Sunday
4a	Lord of all peace
5a	Recognition of our calling
6a	Lord of Love
8a	Lord of all Grace
13a	Jesus welcomes and includes people
14a	Collect for Good Friday
15a	Rejoicing in God .... Luke 1:46–47
17a	The Creator .... Genesis 1:1
19a	From Everlasting to Everlasting .. 1 Chron 29:10–13
20a	Help from the Lord .... From Psalm 73
22a	Your presence
23a	Praise the Lord .... Psalm 150:6
24a	Songs of Joy .... Psalm 65:8
32a	Jesus shows us Mercy and Grace
34a	Circle me Lord
35a	Living with God .... Psalm 61:4
38a	The Lord has established his throne .... Psalm 103:19
42a	Streams of grace
43a	Come and see
50a	Lord be with ...
51a	Wait for the Lord .... Psalm 27:13–14
52a	The Easter Anthems
53a	Jesus Christ is Lord .... Philippians 2: 10–11
54a	One thing I have asked of the Lord
60a	Christ as a Light
61a	Every Spiritual Blessing .... Ephesians 1:3
63a	Saved by Grace .... Ephesians 2:8–10
65a	Bread of Heaven
66a	Blessing for the Journey
67a	The God who made the world .... Acts 17:24–28
71a	Opening prayer for Easter Sunday
73a	The Lords Prayer
78a	Glory to the Lamb .... Revelation 5:13
81a	The leading and direction of God. Psalm 119:33–35
82a	Memorial of the Resurrection – Prima Luce
83a	Made Alive with Christ .... Colossians 2:13
85a	A Prayer of Confession
86a	A Telling Place
87a	You did that for me
89a	The fullness of Christ .... Ephesians 3:14–19
93a	To Him who is able .... Ephesians 3:20–21
95a	Come from Heaven, Living Bread.... From John 6:51
100a	A Creed .... From Ephesians 3
102a	Prayer of Humble Access
103a	Come and see Jesus ....From John 1:35–51 & 4:1–39
105a	True Worshippers
113a	Jesus - the Living Bread
114a	Belonging .... 1 Peter 2:9–10
115a	Circle us
117a	God about me
120a	You are my Fortress
122a	Lord of all Grace
124a	Christ with us
125a	Showered with love .... From Ephesians 1: 1–14
126a	A Shout of Joy .... From Luke 24:6
130a	True humility
131a	God's transforming power
135a	All that I do
136a	Keep us silent before you..... Based on Revelation 8:1
138a	We have come
140a	A Blessing of Grace .... Ephesians 6:24
142a	Always giving thanks .... From Ephesians 5:19–20
143a	A Prayer of Service
144a	The Mercy of God .... Lamentations 3:22–23
146a	Collect of Easter Sunday
147a	Irish Blessing
148a	Compassionate and Gracious God... From Exodus 34:6
150a	A Trinitarian Blessing .... 2 Corinthians 13:14

Index

Song titles differing from first lines are in italics

Song Title	No	Song Title	No
A love so amazing	6	For every child	35
A love so undeserved	7	For every disappointment	36
A mouth to sing	10	For the grace of God	37
A touching place	*22*	*Forever*	*38*
A word is spoken	17	*Forgiven I stand*	*60*
Above all else	*77*		
Above all powers	1	Give thanks to the Lord	38
Across the lands	*146*	Glory to him	39
All around your throne	2	God of grace	41
All I am Lord	4	God of the mountains	40
All of me	*4*	*God of wonders*	*91*
All of you	5	Good and gracious	42
All you have done	*80*	*Grace*	*90*
Alleluia, sing to Jesus	3	Grace and mercy	43
Amazing	*7*	Great and wonderful	44
Amazing grace	8 & 9	Great is your faithfulness	45
Anthem of the free	*124*		
As high as the heavens	11	*Hallelujah*	*147*
As if you were not there	12	He is good	46
As we gather	13	*He is Yahweh*	*133*
Ashes to beauty	*14*	Hear my prayer, O Lord	47
At the foot of the cross	14	*Hear our prayer*	*35*
Awake, awake	16	Here I am	48
Awake, my soul	15	*Here I am to worship*	*83*
		Here I am, my God	49
		Hide me now	50
Be glorified	*32*	*Highest praise*	*103*
Be lifted up	19	Holy God	51
Beautiful One	*135*	Holy One	53
Befriended	18	Holy, holy God Almighty	52
Better than life	*148*	*How does it feel?*	*58*
Blessed be your name	20	How good it is	54
Christ be before me	21	I can only imagine	55
Christ, be our light!	*85*	*I could not leave this place*	*99*
Christ's is the world	22	I have been crucified with Christ	56
Come on everybody	23	I have no-one in heaven but you	57
Come praise the Lord	24	I kneel in wonder	58
Come, wounded healer	25	I live my life to worship you	59
Consuming fire	*122*	*I know you love me*	*64*
Created to worship	*142*	I love you with all of my heart	60
Creation praise	*40*	I rejoiced when they said to me	66
Cross of Jesus	26	I wait for the Lord	68
Crown of glory, crown of thorns	27	I want to know	69
Crucified with Christ	*56*	I will return to you	71
		I worship you	70
Dance, dance	28	*If you are weary*	*46*
Do something beautiful	*128*	I'm making melody in my heart to you	61
Draw me nearer	*69*	I'm trading my sorrows	62
		In Christ alone	63
Enough	*5*	In every day that dawns	64
Everlasting	30	Into the centre	65
Everlasting God	29	It is by your mighty power	67
Every breath	*24*		
		Jesus Christ, you are the Son of God	72
Faithful and true	31	Jesus is Lord	75
Faithful, mighty, glorious	*51*	Jesus melt my cold heart	76
Famous one	*138*	Jesus you alone	79
Father let me dedicate	32	Jesus, be the centre	73
Father we have sinned	33	Jesus, I've forgotten	74
Father your love is a faithful love	34		

Song Title	No
Jesus, my passion in life	77
Jesus, the very thought of thee	78
Joy is in this place	*28*
Just to be with you	*59*
King of kings	*139*
King of the ages	80
Kingdom come	*108*
Lead me on Lord	81
Let my words be few	*136*
Let the heavens rejoice	*19*
Let the living stones cry out	82
Let us go to the house of the Lord	*66*
Light of the world	83
Like a mighty river	84
Longing for light	85
Looking for your presence	86
Lord have mercy	*74*
Lord here we stand	87
Lord I come before your throne	88
Lord of all creation	91
Lord turn your footsteps	92
Lord you are good	93
Lord, I come	89
Lord, I'm grateful	90
Lost in wonder	*140*
Majesty	*48*
May the love of Christ	94
Mercy flows	95
My desire	*131*
My heart is filled with thankfulness	96
My hope	*137*
My Lord, you wore no royal crown	97
My soul rejoices	*23*
My souls desire	98
No one else is worthy	*107*
Nothing could take your love away	99
O for a thousand tongues	100
O God of grace	101
O the deep, deep love of Jesus	104
On my knees	*72*
Open arms	*71*
Open the eyes of my heart	102
Opening our hearts to you	103
Our God is a great big God	105
Outrageous grace	*123*
Pour over me	*149*
Praise the Lord	107
Praise the Lord from the heavens	106
Psalm 148	*106*
Rebuild your temple	108
Repentance	*33*
Resurrection hymn	*110*
Rise up my soul and sing	*15*
Risen One	*53*
Saviour	109
Say the word	*17*

Song Title	No
See, what a morning	110
Show us your glory	*130*
Sing to the Lord	111
Sovereign Lord	112
Still	*36*
Still	*50*
Take me deeper	*76*
Take my life and let it be	113
Tender Saviour	115
Thank you for the cross, Lord	114
The Lord is gracious and compassionate	116
The love of God comes close	117
The voice of hope	*11*
There are shadows across the sun	118
There is a higher throne	119
There is a hope so sure	120
There is a new song	*132*
There is a river	121
There must be more than this	122
There's a lot of pain	123
This is my Jesus	*31*
This is the anthem of the free	124
This is the day	*10*
This is what I live to do	*70*
This is you	*141*
Though I've seen troubles	126
Through days of rage and wonder	125
To God our great salvation	127
To the one God	*118*
Unchanging	*45*
We are a shining light	128
We are bowed before you	130
We come in your name	129
We crown you now	*39*
What a faithful God have I	*88*
What a Saviour	*109*
What wonder of grace is this	131
When I was lost	132
Who is moving on the waters	133
Wonderful grace	134
Wonderful Maker	*144*
Wonderful, so wonderful	135
Worthy is the Lamb	*114*
Yes, Lord	*62*
Yesterday, today, forever	*29*
You are God in heaven	136
You are righteous	137
You are the Lord, the famous one	138
You came from heaven	139
You chose the cross	140
You colour this world beautiful	141
You formed us from the dust	142
You have been lifted	*129*
You know	*65*
You pour out grace	143
You spread out the skies	144
Your love is amazing	147
Your love is everlasting	148
Your love shining like the sun	149
Your loving kindness	150
You're King and you reign	145
You're the word of God the Father	146

Addresses of copyright holders

Beracah Music International. info@beracahmusic.com

Bishop Timothy Dudley Smith, 9 Ashlands, Ford, Salisbury, Wiltshire, SP4 6DY, UK

brownbearMusic,154 Deptford High Street, London, SE8 3PQ, UK

Bucks Music Ltd., 11 Uxbridge Street, London W8 7TQ, UK

CopyCare, P.O. Box 77, Hailsham, East Sussex, BN27 3EF, UK. music@copycare.com

Daybreak Music Ltd. P.O. Box 2848, Eastbourne, BN20 7XP, UK. info@daybreakmusic.co.uk

IQ Music Ltd, Commercial House, 52 Perrymount Road, Haywards Heath, West Sussex RH16 3DT, UK

Jubilate Hymns, 4 Thorne Park Road, Chelston, Torquay, TQ2 6RX, UK

Kevin Mayhew Ltd, Buxhall, Stowmarket, Suffolk, IP14 3BW, UK

Kingsway's Thankyou Music, P.O. Box 75, Lottbridge Drove, Eastbourne, East Sussex, BN23 6NT, UK. tym@kingsway.co.uk.

Lensongs Publishing, 287 Spout Springs Road, Muscle Shoals, AL35661, USA

Make Way Music, P.O. Box 263, Croydon, Surrey, CR9 5AP, UK

OCP Publications, 5536 NE Hassalo, Portland OR 97213, USA

Sovereign Music UK, PO Box 356, Leighton Buzzard, Beds., LU7 8WP, UK. sovereignmusic@aol.com

Wild Goose Resource Group (WGRG), The Iona Community, Glasgow, G2 3DH, Scotland